PUFFIN BOOKS

Editor: Kaye Webb

THE JUNIOR PUFFIN QUIZ BOOK

THE JUNIOR PUFFIN
QUIZ
BOOK

Norman and Margaret Dixon

PENGUIN BOOKS

Penguin Books Ltd, Harmondsworth, Middlesex, England
Penguin Books Inc., 7110 Ambassador Road, Baltimore, Maryland 21207, U.S.A.
Penguin Books Australia Ltd, Ringwood, Victoria, Australia

—

First published 1966
Reprinted 1967, 1969, 1970

—

Copyright © Norman and Margaret Dixon, 1966

—

Cover design by Jill McDonald

—

Made and printed in Great Britain by
Cox & Wyman Ltd,
London, Reading and Fakenham
Set in Monotype Times

QUESTIONS

1. This is question one in the first set of questions. Can you add the second half of each of these proverbs, which all contain the word 'one'?
    (a) One man's meat . . .
    (b) One swallow . . .
    (c) One good turn . . .

2. Who wore Lincoln Green?

3. Where in London would you go to see the Crown Jewels? What rather uncommon birds might you see just outside the place where the jewels are kept?

4. 'The kettle is boiling,' said the boy. 'I can see steam coming out of the spout.'
    What is incorrect in the boy's statement?

5. What do we call the use of words to suggest different meanings which you can see twice in this verse by Thomas Hood writing about a sailor?

    'His death, which happen'd in his berth,
        At forty-odd befell:
    They went and told the sexton, and
        The sexton toll'd the bell.'

6. 'Dr — , I presume!' What explorer greeted what great nineteenth-century missionary in Africa in this way?

7. Can you give three different names for places where monks or nuns live?

8. What English bird makes its nest on the bare ground and rises high into the air singing as it climbs?

9. Can you complete the following saying of Jesus Christ?
   – 'What shall it profit a man if he shall gain . . .?'

10. Which of these years are leap years? – 1900, 1960, 1965, 1970, 2000.

1. In what island was the city of Knossos? What was the name of the king who ruled there? What monster was supposed to be housed there and in what place did he live? What Greek hero is said to have killed him?

2. Of what countries is the dragon the symbol? A number of men are said to have killed dragons. Can you give the name of one of them?

3. Can you arrange in order of size from the smallest upwards a cello, a double-bass, a violin, and a viola?

4. What flower did Lord Tennyson call 'February fair-maid'? Do you think the description is a good one?

5. What is a Big Top? Where would you find the big end? What is it?

6. How would you work out the average of five numbers?

7. Apart from the actual injury what is the greatest danger to a person who has met with an accident?

8. Who might boast about 'doing a hole in one'? What would he mean?

9. What well-known substance comes from the trees of prehistoric forests?

10. Which of these towns and cities are not in England? – Cardiff, Carlisle, Glasgow, Liverpool, Llandudno, Shrewsbury.

1. What is cornflour obtained from?

2. In what country is Snowdonia? In what general direction would you go from London to reach it? – NE, NW, W, SE, or SW.

3. In what novel is John Ridd the central male figure?

4. If you add together the number of the testaments in the Bible, the number of the commandments and the number of the gospels, what is the answer?

5. For what can you obtain a Black Belt?

6. What is the difference between iron and steel?

7. What do the following abbreviations stand for? To what class do they all belong? – Ag, Au, Cu, Fe, N.

8. What is a census? Have you ever been concerned in one?

9. In old history books the queen who reigned from 1558 to 1603 is referred to simply as Elizabeth. When did we start calling her Elizabeth I?

10. Can you give the names the Greeks or the Romans had for the messengers of the gods? (There were three of them.)

1. What does a person usually have to obtain before he can enter a foreign country?

2. Is Zanzibar off the east or the west coast of Africa?

3. What is a washer on a tap like? What is its purpose?

4. What tree in this country sometimes retains its brown withered leaves all through the winter?

5. Can you arrange the following famous men in the order in which they lived? – Julius Caesar, Mohammed, St Paul, William the Conqueror, Xerxes.

6. Who said 'One more step, Mr Hands, and I'll blow your brains out!'? What was happening?

7. Where do the Moors live? Where did the Mohawks and the Senecas live?

8. What is the difference between a bob-sleigh and a toboggan?

9. Has Spain a coastline on the Atlantic Ocean or on the Mediterranean Sea? Which does Portugal have?

10. What are the titles given to the two most important bishops in the Church of England?

1. Who lived in a cottage that contained a corkindrill hanging from the rafters, a reputed phoenix which smelt of incense and cinnamon, six live grass snakes, an ordinary beehive, two young hedgehogs in cotton-wool, a gold medal for being the best scholar at Winchester, the fourteenth edition of the Encyclopaedia Britannica, six pismires, a complete set of cigarette cards depicting wild fowl by Peter Scott, and many other things?

2. Two explorers pitched their tent in a place where each of the four walls faced south. Where were they?

3. Can you give the names of two Presidents of the United States who were assassinated? Have any English sovereigns since 1066 been assassinated?

4. What is a fossil? Where might you expect to find one?

5. What grows in a paddy field? Paddy is also the nickname for a member of a certain nation. What nation is it?

6. A train $\frac{1}{2}$ mile long passes through a tunnel $\frac{1}{2}$ mile long at 60 m.p.h. How long does it take to pass through?

7. If a violinist was playing *pizzicato*, what would he be doing?

8. What is studied in the science of meteorology? What is another name for a meteor? What is the difference between a meteor and a meteorite?

9. How did the meal 'breakfast' get its name? Was there a meal called 'tea' in England during the Middle Ages? What meal is 'brunch'?

10. Who said to whom on what occasion: 'This night, before the cock crow, thou shalt deny me thrice'? Did the prophecy come true?

1. What are the names given to the places in which live cowboys, doves, passengers on a ship, rabbits, and soldiers?

2. Of what city has it been said that 'the sea is the street there'? What is the name given to the boats that ply for hire in the canals of this city?

3. What is a beagle?

4. Can you think of three painters whose names begin with V?

5. 'Thar she blows!' What person would use this exclamation? What does it mean?

6. What is the meaning of the initials G.P.O.?

7. What is *crêpe* paper? And what is *crêpe* hair?

8. Who is supposed to have said on his death-bed 'Kiss me, Hardy'?

9. What is camber?

10. How many cents are there in the American dollar, dime, and nickel?

1. What is a rodeo?

2. Through which of these countries does the river Rhine flow? – Austria, Belgium, France, Germany, Holland, Italy, Switzerland.

3. What is it that runs along a permanent way? You might say that any road is a permanent way, but the name is always applied to one particular thing.

4. With what country is T. E. Lawrence associated?

5. Six of the following football clubs can be arranged in pairs which have their grounds fairly near each other. What are the pairs? – Arsenal, Aston Villa, Blackburn Rovers, Birmingham, Everton, Luton, Liverpool, Tottenham Hotspur.

6. What is second sight?

7. Can you give the names of three English wild animals that live underground?

8. On what vehicle and to what destination did Skimble-shanks travel? What sort of creature was he?

9. Which of the following do you associate with the Red Indians? – boomerang, bungalow, moccasin, ski, squaw, tepee, trek, wigwam.

10. In what hobby is a perforation gauge used?

8

1. What rank is a policeman who has three stripes on his arm?

2. Can you name half a dozen places on the road where you should not overtake when you are on a cycle or driving a car?

3. What is a hamburger? What connexion has it with ham?

4. Is the zither a stringed instrument?

5. Whereabouts in the body is the retina situated?

6. There are sixteen teams taking part in a football knock-out competition. How many matches must be played to find the winning team, assuming there are no drawn games?

7. Can you complete these phrases: (i) Out of the frying-pan . . . (ii) Six of one . . . (iii) Least said . . . (iv) Out of sight . . .

8. In what cities are the official residences of the Pope and the President of the United States?

9. What is done by a combine harvester?

10. Who was Venus?

1. At what time approximately does the sun rise and set in this country towards the end of March and the end of September? At what points of the compass does it rise and set?

2. What coins were called a tanner, a bob and a quid?

3. Here is a number: 142,857. What happens when it is multiplied by 2, 3, 4, 5, or 6? What happens when it is multiplied by 7?

4. Can you give the names of three leaders of the Crusades?

5. What makes a dachshund look different from other dogs?

6. In what continents are Normandy, Queensland, Ontario and Texas situated?

7. When is Shrove Tuesday? What is traditionally done on that day?

8. What gas was used to fill the early airships? Today another gas is used which is not as light as the gas that was first used. What is the name of this gas? Why is it used instead of the other one?

9. Where do real pearls come from? How are they produced?

10. What are M1 and M.I.5?

1. In what cities are there very famous churches dedicated to St Mark, St Paul, St Peter, and Santa Sophia?

2. What is a Boeing 707? What is a Boeing 747?

3. What is the Ordnance Survey?

4. What great eighteenth-century writer compiled a famous dictionary?

5. Hartnell, Yves St Laurent and Chanel are all famous for the same sort of work. What is it?

6. Which common English bird has a bright yellow beak? And which has a speckled breast?

7. Oxford and Cambridge are the most famous English universities. What universities occupy a corresponding place in the United States?

8. Would a Martian find it easy to move about if he landed on the earth?

9. What is the meaning of the letters E.R.? Where are you most likely to see them?

10. Shakespeare wrote in one of his songs: 'When roasted crabs hiss in the bowl.' What sort of crabs was he referring to? What was in the bowl besides the crabs?

11

1. What is a dig? What are digs? What is a digger?

2. Can you complete the following sayings?
    (i) A peck of March dust . . .
    (ii) When the wind is in the . . .
        It's good . . .

3. What is a motel? How is the word formed?

4. Where would you expect to see pebble-dash? What is it?

5. What is the meaning of 'Erin go bragh!'?

6. Can you give the names of two battles fought in England in which English kings were killed?

7. Can you arrange these mountains in the order of their heights? – Ben Nevis, Everest, Kilimanjaro, Mont Blanc, Snowdon.

8. Who was the wife of King Arthur, and who of Robin Hood?

9. When does lighting-up time for vehicles in this country begin and end?

10. What is the name of the Roman governor before whom Jesus Christ was tried? What questions did he ask of Jesus?

12

1. What is first-aid? What organization exists in this country to provide it?

2. What is on the opposite side of the world to the Arctic regions? If you could dig straight down from England through the centre of the earth, what spot would you come to on the other side?

3. What door opened to the magic phrase 'Open Sesame!'?

4. Who had a servant named Man Friday? How did he come to work for his master?

5. Is it true that the owl and the cat can see in the dark?

6. Where might you see a combination of numbers and letters like ABA231B?

7. Can you give the names of three rulers who have been called The Great?

8. The land where Jesus Christ lived is now divided into two countries. What are their names?

9. What are the two main processes coffee beans go through before they are used?

10. Is there a university called Oxbridge?

1. What is the name of the great sports and athletics centre in London?

2. Can you add the next three terms to each of the following series?
   - (i)   12, 8, 4 . . .
   - (ii) 27, 9, 3 . . .
   - (iii) 7, 8, 10, 13, 17 . . .

3. Generals de Gaulle, Eisenhower, MacArthur, Rommel and Wavell were all famous generals of the Second World War. To what countries did they belong?

4. Is Janus the name of (a) a Greek hero; (b) a make of car; (c) a group of islands; (d) a Roman god; or (e) a man-made fabric?

5. What are the Mounties?

6. If you sailed down the river Thames towards the sea, you would pass through, among others, these towns – Henley, London, Oxford, Maidenhead, Reading. What is the order in which you would reach them?

7. What are the four kinds of grain (or corn) commonly grown in the British Isles? What other is often seen in the United States?

8. What is the word missing from the two blanks in these lines that begin a poem by Robert Burns? (The same word is needed for each blank.)

   'My heart's in the . . . my heart is not here,
   My heart's in the . . . a-chasing the deer.'

9. How much milk is contained in (a) a standard milk bottle and (b) a school milk bottle?

10. Does the ash from a coal fire do good to the garden?

1. The following are different forms of the name 'John'. In what countries are they used? – Giovanni, Ian, Ivan, Jean, Johann, Juan, Sean.

2. What is a Clearway?

3. With what other man and with what expedition do you associate Sir Henry Curtis and Captain John Good?

4. In what sort of place is there a skirting board?

5. What was the most famous battle won by the Duke of Wellington? In what year was it fought?

6. What is the order in which these courses would be served at a formal dinner? – cheese, coffee, entrée, *hors d'œuvres*, fish, roast, soup, sweet.

7. Who unpicked every night the tapestry that she had woven during the day? Why did she do this?

8. What edible shell-fish are found in the waters round the English coast?

9. How does the penknife get its name?

10. (a) What is the name of the strait where Europe and Africa come closest together?
    (b) What continents are separated by the Behring Strait?

1. Whose day is 14 February?

2. Can you give two other older names for the city which is now called Istanbul? Where is it situated?

3. What is a tinder? What was a tinder-box used for?

4. Where is Table Mountain?

5. Why do you sometimes see red number plates on cars?

6.
> His queer long coat from heel to head
> Was half of yellow and half of red,
> And he himself was tall and thin,
> With sharp blue eyes, each like a pin.'

   Who is described in this quotation? What did he undertake to do, and what was his fee?

7. Who was Circe? What powers did she have?

8. What foods do horses usually eat? What things are given to them as delicacies?

9. Where is the line of life to be seen?

10. In what countries is Esperanto spoken?

16

1. Who rode on the footplate in the days of steam engines?

2. Three of the following districts are not in London. Which are they? – Battersea, Bermondsey, Dulwich, Islington, Kensington, Knightsbridge, Headingley, Moss Side, Soho, Solihull.

3. Where does the death-watch beetle live? How did it get its name?

4. What do you know about Frankenstein?

5. What does a building society build?

6. Which of these artists are Italian? – Gauguin, Goya, Michelangelo, Raphael, Rubens, Titian.

7. Is brisket the name of a hold in wrestling, part of a car engine, a joint of meat, or a dive?

8. What great general was an ancestor of Sir Winston Churchill?

9. What are the names of the two famous Glasgow football clubs?

10. What qualities does aluminium have that give it an advantage over most other metals? Is there any difference between aluminium and aluminum?

1. Was any type of armoured vehicle used in the First World War?

2. Does a compass always point in the same direction?

3. What is the significance of the flashing amber light sometimes seen on the top of a vehicle on the road?

4. Though the body is dead, what goes marching on?

5. In what island was Napoleon I born? On what island did he die? What was his surname?

6. What would you look up in Gibbons' Catalogue?

7. What is an eisteddfod? (Is the word spelled correctly?) In what country is it usually held?

8. Where was Mount Olympus and who lived on it?

9. Which is greater:
    (a) 9 dozen, or 5 score?
    (b) half of half of half of 24, or $\frac{1}{4}$ dozen?
    (c) 239 pence, or 479 halfpence?
    (d) 5 less than 21 more than 13, or $\frac{1}{2}$ of 5×12?
    (e) $2 \times 2 \times 2 \times 2 \times 2$, or $3 \times 3 \times 3 \times 3$?
    (f) the number of pence in 6s 11d or the number of inches in 2 yds 1 ft?

10. Can you give the names of the organs in our body which act as a pump and as bellows?

18

1. Can you name three places in which you might see a fender? Is its purpose the same in each case?

2. Make a 'magic square' by filling in the spaces with the numbers from 1 to 9, so that each row (across, down, and diagonally) totals 15.

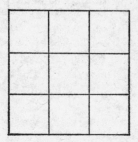

3. What is a V.I.P.?

4. Who complained: 'You have baked me too brown, I must sugar my hair'? And who 'wept like anything to see such quantities of sand'?

5. Of what city is Montmartre a famous part? Where is St Michael's Mount?

6. Every hour a train leaves Whatton for Whybury, and at the same time one leaves Whybury on its way to Whatton. The journey to Whybury takes exactly two hours. How many trains from Whybury could a passenger see on the journey?

7. What is the story behind the phrase 'the Achilles heel'? How is the phrase used nowadays?

8. What is the name given to the species of cat which has a cream-coloured body, dark chocolate ears, face, legs, and tail, blue eyes and a small head?

9. What English artist is famous for his paintings of Salisbury Cathedral and Flatford Mill?

10. In what country did the Pharaohs rule?

1. If a person is suffering from insomnia, what does he find it difficult to do?

2. A mitre can be two things. What are they?

3. Where is Lindisfarne? Do you know another name for it?

4. Who heard bells telling him to turn again? What bells were they? What did they prophesy?

5. What is a mayday message? How did the name arise?

6. In the imaginary land of Sixteria, the people count in sixes instead of tens. Can you do their arithmetic?

   (a)

Sixes	Units
2	3
+1	4
-----	-----

   (b)

Sixes	Units
4	0
-2	1
-----	-----

   (c)

   25
   × 3

   ---

7. What do the symbols H_2O represent?

8. Is there such a thing as a four leafed clover, and what do some people believe about it? What other meaning does the word clover-leaf have nowadays besides referring to the plant?

9. Where do 'the mountains of Mourne look down to the sea'?

10. What was the language spoken by Julius Caesar? In what language did St Paul write his epistles (or letters)?

1. What do pattens look like? What were they used for in the old days?

2. If two red lights appear at the back of a car in the day-time, what is their significance?

3. Was poison-gas used at any time during the Second World War?

4. What is made in these sizes? – 8 mm., 9·5 mm., 16 mm., 35 mm., and 70 mm.?

5. What is the original meaning of the word 'piano-forte'?

6. In what country are there gendarmes? What work do they do?

7. What city is the capital of Wales?

8. With what stories do you associate Haroun-al-Raschid? Was he a real person?

9. What is hitch-hiking? What is thumbing a lift?

10. John has nine coins. They all look alike, but one is a little lighter than the others. He wants to discover which is the odd one, and his uncle lends him a balance without weights, and tells him to use it for only two weighings. How does he do it?

1. Over what country does the King of the Hellenes rule?

2. What people are said in verse to have gone to sea, but not in boats?

3. What is four-wheel independent suspension?

4. What sort of creature is a marmoset? What is a marmot? A marmot in America has another name. Do you know a tongue-twister in which this name plays an important part?

5. If $\frac{1}{2} + \frac{1}{4} = \frac{3}{4}$, $\frac{1}{2} + \frac{1}{4} + \frac{1}{8} = \frac{7}{8}$, $\frac{1}{2} + \frac{1}{4} + \frac{1}{8} + \frac{1}{16} = \frac{15}{16}$ what is $\frac{1}{2} + \frac{1}{4} + \frac{1}{8} + \frac{1}{16} + \frac{1}{32}$?

6. Is a licence needed for keeping a dog? Is one needed for a cat? For a horse?

7. Who was the first jockey to be knighted? And the first cricketer? And the first footballer?

8. Under what name is St Nicholas better known?

9. You probably know the line in a nursery rhyme 'Here comes a big chopper to chop off your head'. But do you know for what 'chopper' is the modern nickname? And if you do can you give another nickname for it?

10. Who in the old days might finish up at Tyburn?

22

1. Where was Shakespeare born?

2. Is it an offence against the law to play football in the public street?

3. Whereabouts was the ancient city of Troy situated? Was it in Europe or in Asia? What was another name for it?

4. What is a slalom?

5. Which railway station in London would you arrive at if you were travelling up from Cornwall?

6. Where would you see a wind-sock?

7. From what grain is bread usually made in this country?

8. What did the Good Samaritan do? What is the point in the parable of his being a Samaritan?

9. When a baby is born what legal formality must be carried out within six weeks?

10. 'Now . . .
   Is seen the fair, sweet, chastened face of May;
   She is the daughter of the year who stands
   With Autumn's last rich offerings in her hands.'

How can you tell that this does not refer to England? What month in England corresponds to May in this poem?

1. Is it an acid or an alkali that turns blue litmus paper red?

2. Is a psaltery (a) the book of Psalms; (b) a kind of musical instrument; (c) a term used in heraldry; or (d) a kind of fossil?

3. What are the names of the first two letters of the ancient Greek alphabet? What common English word comes directly from them?

4. What is the name given to the group of three soldiers— Porthos, Athos, and Aramis? Who was their companion?

5. What is the Union Pacific?

6. How is sand produced?

7. What does a newspaper man mean by a scoop?

8. If a man lived in the West Riding what county would his home be in?

9. To whom, according to the Bible, were the Ten Commandments given by God? Where did this happen?

10. Can you arrange these families of English kings in the order in which they reigned? – Lancastrian, Norman, Plantagenet, Stuart, Tudor, Windsor.

1. What famous cities are situated on the rivers Seine and Tagus?

2. If you were given some castanets what would you probably do with them?

3. What is the name of the biggest planet in the Solar System? How many moons has it?

4. For how many days, according to the first chapter of Genesis, did God work to accomplish the creation? What did God do on the next day?

5. Butter and cheese are both made from milk. What is the difference in the way in which they are prepared?

6. Many aeroplanes are powered by jet engines, a fairly recent invention, but jet propulsion has been used by some sea creatures for thousands of years. What are these creatures?

7. 'Four gray walls and four gray towers
   Overlook a space of flowers,
   And the silent isle imbowers' . . . (Whom?)

8. Why is there the notice 'Air Brakes' sometimes to be seen on the back of a lorry?

9. Which of the following plants are grown from bulbs?—Chrysanthemum, lupin, poppy, snowdrop, tulip.

10. An army commander knew that the enemy were sheltering at the foot of a cliff which was somewhere in front of him and his men. It was a very dark night, yet he had to know quickly how far away the cliff was. He told one of his men to fire a shot into the air, and a few seconds later he announced that the enemy were about 700 yards ($\frac{2}{5}$ mile) away. How did he know? It should be mentioned that he had a stop watch.

1. Where were the Spice Islands of the Middle Ages?

2. What man returned to England on 26 May 1660 amid general rejoicing? How had he come to leave this country?

3. What is joined by a joiner?

4. What weapon does an English policeman carry on normal duty?

5. What is Interpol?

6. Who wrote 'She Stoops to Conquer'?

7. A furniture van became wedged under a low bridge, and no attempts to free it by using the engine did any good. How did the driver free it without any outside aid and with little trouble?

8. Who climbed a hill to fetch some water? And who saw

    'Water, water, everywhere,
    Nor any drop to drink'?

9. What were the names of the Roman god of the sun, and the Roman goddess of the moon?

10. How does an auction differ from ordinary buying and selling?

1. In some towns in England like York there is a street called The Shambles. How did it get this name?

2. From what is leather made? What is the name given to the process of preparing it?

3. What can be done with a burning glass?

4. How many queen bees are there in a hive at any one time?

5. In what approximate directions would the shadow of a tree lie in this country when the sun was rising in the middle of summer and when it was rising in the middle of winter?

6. Who were the commandos?

7. If in a restaurant you ordered '*pommes de terre frites*', what would the waiter bring you?

8. What is the name of the river that is formed by the joining together of the Trent, the Yorkshire Ouse and other streams?

9. What well-known children's book begins in this way?– 'Roger, aged seven, and no longer the youngest of the family, ran in wide zigzags, to and fro, across the steep field that sloped up from the lake to Holly Howe, the farm where they were staying for part of the summer holidays.'

10. 'Phew!' said Mr Smith, wiping the sweat from his brow. 'This July heat is really unbearable, and these monsoon showers do little to cool you off. I wish I could return to the prairies of Canada.' 'I agree with you about the heat,' said his friend, 'but I thought the temperature on the prairies was in the 80s as it is here.' 'True,' said Mr Smith, 'but the dry heat of Canada is quite comfortable.'

Why was Mr Smith right?

1. Where were gnomes originally supposed to live? What was their work?

2. Who were Parnesius and Pertinax?

3. What happened on D-Day? What was its date?

4. Which of these are prehistoric animals? – Armadillo, ichneumon, ichthyosaurus, iguana, iguanodon, mastodon, pterodactyl.

5. What is a 'blue'? What is the difference between a 'light blue' and a 'dark blue'? What are the Blues?

6. Who killed what giant by a stone sent from a sling?

7. From what is sugar obtained?

8. With what clubs do you associate grounds at Trent Bridge?

9. What is the name given to the part sung by the boys in a choir?

10. What city, badly bombed during the Second World War, is a centre of the British car industry? What city is the centre of the American car industry?

1. If a man goes 'on safari' what is his purpose? In what continent would he probably go?

2. What island is joined to the mainland by the Menai Bridge? What is the mainland?

3. What are triffids?

4. How many meanings can you give of the word 'chaps'?

5. Do fish bring forth their young alive, or do they lay eggs?

6. After whom are Wednesday, March and July named?

7. If a cook made a *soufflé*, what sort of thing would it be?

8. What, according to the proverb, may look at a king?

9. What is a vegetarian? What does he refuse to do?

10. What is meant by 'buzzing' a plane?

1. Numerals like C, D and M are called Roman numerals.
   What is the value of C, D and M in ordinary numerals?
   What is the name we give to numerals like 3, 5 and 9?

2. Were root crops like turnips and swedes grown in
   England during the Middle Ages?

3. John Masefield wrote of a –

   'Stately Spanish galleon coming from the Isthmus,
   Dipping through the Tropics by the palm-green shores.'

   What isthmus was it? What was the galleon carrying?

4. What does *née* mean in such a phrase as Mrs W. B.
   Johnstone (*née* Marsden)?

5. What change has been brought about by the use of
   germanium?

6. What is pasta? How many varieties of it can you name?

7. For what is Dunkirk famous in British history?

8. What is a metronome? What is it used for?

9. It has been said that Le Mans 'hits the headlines every
   year in June'. Why is this?

10. What was or is a siren?

1. Why, in classical times, did people go to Delphi?

2. In the answer to a question in the previous paper there occurred the word 'moidores'. What was a moidore?

3. Are Shanghai and Tokyo in China or Japan?

4. What articles of clothing do you connect with duffle, dirndl, and stetson?

5. Which of the following animals hibernate? – fox, hedgehog, mouse, rabbit, rat, squirrel.

6. What are bifocal glasses?

7. What was the real name of Bonny Prince Charlie? Do you know a third name for him? With what episode is he specially connected?

8. The story goes that a lady once taunted a wealthy man for being mean with his money. The man replied by writing out a cheque for £100 and throwing it into the fire, remarking that it showed he was willing to burn money. What can you say about this?

9. What Italian alive 450 years ago was a very great artist and sculptor, wrote poetry, designed part of St Peter's Cathedral in Rome and painted the frescoes in the Sistine Chapel?

10. How was the Pole Star a help to sailors? What is the name of the constellation that has two stars pointing towards the Pole Star?

1. Who organized a caucus race? What was there peculiar about it?

2. What counties lie to the east and to the west of the Pennines?

3. What things are measured in deniers and in watts?

4. What is a supersonic aircraft? What is there peculiar about such an aircraft?

5. A footballer, taking a penalty, hit the cross-bar with the ball and then scored direct from the rebound. The referee disallowed the goal. Why?

6. To what men is the title 'whip' given?

7. What is a bantam?

8. What is Swan Lake?

9. In what part of the United States do most of the Negroes live? How did their ancestors come to the States?

10. In what wars did the British armies fight the battles of the Somme and El Alamein?

1. One of the answers in the last set mentioned a dodo. What sort of creature is this? Do you know a common phrase in which the word is used?

2. An anemometer indicated a speed of force 11 on the Beaufort scale. What is an anemometer? What is the approximate speed of force 11?

3. What is a clam? If you say a person is a clam what do you mean?

4. To what piece of land has the name 'No Man's Land' been specially applied?

5. Were Ireland and Scotland ever parts of the Roman Empire?

6. What are the famous cities on the Ganges and the Nile?

7. 'I have some papers here,' said my friend ... as we sat one winter's night on either side of the fire, 'which I really think ... it would be worth your while to glance over. These are the documents in the extraordinary case of the *Gloria Scott*, and this is the message which struck Justice of the Peace Trevor dead with horror when he read it.'
Who is speaking to whom?

8. Which is the lighter in these pairs of metals? – (a) Silver and platinum; (b) Gold and nickel.

9. Where did the Philistines live? Whose enemies were they?

10. If in a football match the referee and a linesman disagree, who makes the final decision?

1. Some people do not believe that Shakespeare wrote the plays ascribed to him. Who do these people believe wrote the plays?

2. What are the two great Communist powers in the world today?

3. What are ordinary cups, saucers and plates made from?

4. Were W. G. Grace's great cricketing days in the nine-teenth or the twentieth century?

5. What brings good luck to a bride?
   Something . . . , something . . . ,
   Something . . . , something . . .

6. What are elvers?

7. What line in the hymn comes just before –

   'Our hope for years to come'?

8. Who invaded this country the first in the following pairs? – (a) The Romans and the Celts; (b) the Danes and the Anglo-Saxons; (c) the Anglo-Saxons and the Normans?

9. What are the signals on the bell that a bus conductor gives to the driver?

10. What are a gourmet and a gourmand interested in? Is there any difference between them?

1. If there is an amber light winking at the side of a car, what does this mean?

2. T. S. Eliot wrote a play called *Murder In The Cathedral*. Who was murdered in what cathedral?

3. What are kilns used for?

4. What is the popular name for the plant called myosotis?

5. If ten odd numbers are added together, will the answer be
   (a) Always odd,
   (b) Never odd, or
   (c) Sometimes odd?

6. What connexion is there between Johann Gutenberg and William Caxton?

7. Where did the covered wagon go?

8. How were Ixion, Sisyphus and Tantalus said by the Greeks to be punished after their death?

9. What are the markings on the sides of a dice?

10. Is a metre longer or shorter than a yard? Is a kilogram heavier or lighter than a pound?

1. To what town in Britain did the Romans go to 'take the waters' – that is to drink or bathe in the curative water? Do you know the Roman name for the town?

2. What is a twelfth man?

3. Which dog in each of these pairs is the bigger? – (a) Chow or chihuahua; (b) scottie or saluki; (c) poodle or pekinese.

4. Where is Aswan? Why is it well known?

5. What is the difference between centrifugal and centripetal force?

6. Who killed the fatted calf for whom?

7. Can you think of three things that are named after Queen Victoria? (There are many more than three. Try to think of as many as you can.)

8. Who wrote about Jeeves? What was Jeeves by occupation?

9. What is the approximate weight of a normal baby at birth – 5, 7¼, 10, 12, or 15 pounds?

10. In what part of a house would you see a dormer window?

1. What do you connect with Jodrell Bank and Goonhilly Down?

2. Who uses a stethoscope? What is it for?

3. Who were supposed to drink nectar? What was their food?

4. Sometimes painted in white in the middle of the road there is an arrow with the point curving towards the side. What is meant by this?

5. What exactly is it that is celebrated on 5 November? In what year did this event take place?

6. Is Rome on the coast of Italy? What river is it built on?

7. What bill is J. H. Williams?

8. There is a hymn which begins: 'O little town of Bethlehem.' What event which took place in Bethlehem is celebrated in this?

9. How many balls are there in an over at cricket?

10. What oil is used in oil painting?

1. What are an argonaut, an astronaut, and a cosmonaut?

2. What flowers do we eat?

3. What might be the question to which the answer is '3 September 1939'?

4. Is the nearest land to the Scilly Isles, Brittany, Cornwall, or Pembrokeshire?

5. During what race do those taking part hope to see their rivals all the time? Why?

6. What is the name we give to the supports of overhead electricity power wires?

7. In what country was the dish called curry originally made? Do you know another completely different meaning of the word?

8. Can you fill in the blanks in these quotations from Shakespeare?
   (a) The quality of . . . is not strain'd.
   (b) If . . . be the food of love, play on.
   (c) This royal . . . of kings, this . . . isle,
       This earth of . . . this seat of . . . (Of England)
   (d) I know a bank whereon the wild . . . blows.
   (e) The cowslips tall, her . . . be.

9. For what purpose was Foucault's pendulum used?

10. What do we mean if we call a person a dog in the manger? How did the phrase come about?

1. Who is the most famous woman leader of an army? During what war did she fight?

2. What is the cause of the tides in the sea? What are spring tides and neap tides? Are there any seas in which there are practically no tides?

3. What place in the centre of London is frequented by large flocks of pigeons?

4. Where can you see the Charred Cross? What is it made from?

5. What is pot-holing?

6. What are a frieze, a freesia, and a friesian?

7. What was the name of Hamlet's father in the play by Shakespeare? What command was given to Hamlet by his father's ghost? What was the reason for this order?

8. What letter occurs most frequently in the English language?

9. Can you see a live dinosaur anywhere in the world today?

10. One of the following descriptions is of a Tudor house, and the other is of a Georgian house. Which is which?
    (a) A . . . house is usually irregular in shape, with a gabled roof. It has small casement windows made up of many panes of glass joined by strips

of lead. It is often built of stone or of timber and plaster.

(b) A ... house is usually built of **red** brick on a symmetrical plan. It has large **u**pright sash windows and a handsome doorway, often with a semi-circular fanlight.

1. What type of cloud do glider pilots like best?

2. What animal was generally used for farm work in Europe during the Middle Ages?

3. Was Rupert of Hentzau the hero or the villain in the book by Anthony Hope? Whom did he work against?

4. If a story is danced it is a . . .; if it is sung on the stage it is an . . .; if it is photographed it is a . . .; if it is drawn and then photographed it is an . . .; if it is acted without words it is a . . .. Can you fill in the gaps?

5. What fuels are generally used for cooking in a caravan?

6. What is a frogman? What is the frog's march?

7. Gracie Fields used to sing about 'the biggest aspidistra in the world'. Do you know what an aspidistra is?

8. What is anti-Semitism? It has been common in many countries and in many periods, but during what period and in what country was it specially common?

9. What is the name of the place where Jesus Christ was crucified?

10. What is the material used by the firm of Dunlop to manufacture most of its products?

1. Is a mandrill (a) a musical instrument; (b) an animal; (c) a Chinese dignitary; (d) a poisonous plant; or (e) a vibrating tool?

2. What are Z-cars?

3. Cartridges are used in rifles. Do you know another common thing which is sometimes filled with a cartridge?

4. Do hot air and hot water tend to move upwards or downwards?

5. What three clubs would a golfer probably use if he did a hole in three?

6. Who said of whom that he was 'a freckled whelp hagborn'? Another man said of the same person that he had 'a very ancient and fish-like smell'.

7. On what plain is the famous monument of Stonehenge? What people are supposed to have built it? Is it known from what hills the stones came?

8. Is 'The Laughing Cavalier' the name of a TV adventure series, a painting, a novel by Sir Walter Scott, or a film?

9. What was the original use of the St Bernard dog? How did it come to have this name?

10. A man was opening a greengrocer's shop, and bought a pair of scales second-hand. There were only three weights, 1 lb., 9 lb., and 27 lb., but he realized that if he sometimes put weights in both pans, he needed only one more weight to weigh anything from 1 to 40 lbs. Which weight did he need?

1. What is a cattle-grid? Where might you expect to see one?

2. Here are the descriptions of two wastrels in novels by Charles Dickens; one is Sidney Carton and the other Alfred Jingle. Can you say which is which? In what novels do we read about them?

   (a) An adventurer who talks in a rapid staccato fashion; he fools the hero of the book but is befriended by him when he is in prison.
   (b) A drunken barrister who in the end gives his life to rescue someone from prison.

3. What is the name of the great airport in the Republic of Ireland?

4. For what counties – Gloucestershire, Nottinghamshire, Sussex or Yorkshire – did these cricketers play? – W. Hammond, H. Larwood, M. Tate, W. Rhodes, H. Sutcliffe.

5. What sort of people read Braille?

6. What ships fly the Red Ensign, and what fly the White Ensign?

7. Can you give the names of two well-known castles in North Wales?

8. What is a blood bank?

9. Who cut the Gordian knot? What prophecy was made about the man who could untie this knot?

10. If you knew there was a Portuguese man-of-war about, what action would you probably take?

42

1. Where is the Old Bailey? What do you associate with it?

2. What do you think of when a skunk is mentioned? What sort of creature is it?

3. If a car goes to the pits what is meant?

4. What is a Leica?

5. Can you fill in the blanks in the following? We read in the Bible about two men called Saul. One of them was the first . . . of the . . .; the other changed his name to . . . and is thought to have died a martyr's death in . . .

6. What are the months for fox-hunting in this country? When does cub-hunting begin?

7. Who invited Matilda to come a-waltzing with him?

8. Is Arizona in North or South America?

9. What is meant by going berserk? Who originally went berserk?

10. Is talcum powder animal, vegetable, or mineral?

1. What is a locum tenens? What sort of people make use of one?

2. Of what people was Hiawatha the hero? Who wrote a long poem about him?

3. What is telepathy?

4. Who was thrown into a den of lions? What was it for? Who was swallowed by a whale?

5. Who were supposed to make use of the phrase 'Stand and deliver!'?

6. What two sorts of people might talk about a fairway? What would their meanings be?

7. What are the three countries that together form Scandinavia?

8. Is the weight of this Puffin Quiz Book more or less than half a pound?

9. Where is the Stone of Destiny? Do you know anything about its history and how it came to be where it is?

10. In what city of North America is jazz supposed to have had its origin?

44

1. Can you translate the motto of the Royal Air Force –
'*Per ardua ad astra*'?

2. What creatures suffer from psittacosis?

3. Who was born free? (There are two answers to this.)

4. For what is Easter Island famous?

5. Do you go east or west to reach San Francisco from
Chicago? And do you go north or south to reach New
York from Montreal?

6. Is the present population of the United Kingdom
nearest to 30, 40, 50, or 60 million?

7. If you are somebody's brother-in-law, what relation
is that person to you?

8. What Queen of England ordered the execution of the
Queen of another country?

9. Can you fill in the titles of these books with numbers?
Who wrote the books?
   (a) *Round the World in . . . . . . Days*
   (b) *. . . . . Men in a Boat.*
   (c) *The Sign of . . .*

10. What are seeded players in a tennis tournament?

1. What is plankton?

2. In what country are the Pyramids? Why were they built? Have you any idea how old the largest ones are?

3. In what countries are these cars manufactured? Chevrolet, Fiat, Jaguar, Renault, Volkswagen, Volvo, Zim.

4. Where are the Backs? Where are the Broads?

5. What famous events took place in a building called The Globe? What sort of building was it? Where was it situated?

6. What is the difference between a spade and a shovel?

7. Can you name four countries with which England plays test matches at cricket?

8. Did the United States become independent of Britain in the seventeenth, eighteenth, nineteenth, or twentieth century?

9. Who were the Valkyries? What was their work?

10. What does diesel oil come from?

1. What two countries are separated by the Rio Grande?

2. What is a fell?

3. What flower does Browning call –

> 'the little children's dower
> Far brighter than this gaudy melon flower'?

4. Apart from the 30 or 40 sign, what usually indicates to a motorist that he is in a 30 or 40 m.p.h. speed limit area?

5. What is a Scotch egg? What is the meaning in cricket of a duck's egg?

6. What is usually called 'brackish'? What is the exact meaning of the word?

7. Has the whole of England ever been covered with ice and snow the whole year round?

8. What man lost his strength by having his hair cut off? Who did it?

9. What is alchemy? What were the alchemists trying to do?

10. What is a grace-note?

1. Is the direct distance from Dover to Calais approximately 20, 22, 25, 27 or 30 miles? How long does it take for the Channel steamer to cross?

2. What is the meaning of the phrase 'winning your spurs'? On what famous occasion was it used?

3. What is meant by birds migrating? How do swallows behave when they are getting ready to migrate? Can you name any birds besides those of the swallow family that migrate?

4. What are the cherubim and the seraphim?

5. With what men do you especially associate Cleopatra, Juliet and Helen of Troy?

6. In what city are to be found Trajan's Column and the Trevi Fountain?

7. What is 'homo sapiens'?

8. What club has won the Football Cup the most times?

9. How many words can you think of that end in -ADO, and how many that end in -AGO?

10. If you 'get your cards' what happens to you? What cards are referred to?

1. What city is nearest to Lake Winnipeg? In what country is it?

2. What was the original colour of the lupin? What colours are lupins nowadays?

3. What is the difference between a dictionary and an encyclopaedia?

4. Of what country is Ankara the capital? What things are called after an earlier form of the name of this city?

5. If when you grow up you become a radiographer or a radiotherapist, what would your work be?

6. Who can win an Oscar?

7. What is meant by saying that someone 'carries his bat'?

8. What was the fate of the three blind mice in the nursery rhyme?

9. Was there a year 0 A.D.?

10. A man was originally called 'Shepherd' because he earned his living in a certain way. What way was this? Can you think of any other surnames made in the same way?

1. In how many ways can a lawn-mower be powered?

2. What is a mongoose: bird, animal, fish, or reptile? What is the plural?

3. What countries make up Great Britain?

4. What is the best-known thing about Rip Van Winkle? Where was he supposed to live?

5. Rip Van Winkle came upon some men playing bowls. There are two games called bowls or bowling in this country. Was Rip's game like one of these?

6. What is an inquest? When and why is it held?

7. If in a newspaper report it said that someone was 'allergic to penicillin', what would it mean?

8. If the number of kings of England called Henry, William and George are added together, what is the total?

9. What are the names given to the area over which a bishop is in charge, and to the church with which he is specially connected?

10. Rain falls to the ground because it is subjected to the laws of gravity, but there are occasions when rain, instead of falling, rises at very rapid speeds. When does this happen?

1. What is a smokeless zone? (Perhaps you live in one).

2. What is the difference between a tree and a shrub?

3. One game of bowls was mentioned in the previous set of questions. Where and how is the other game of bowls played?

4. There is a poem by J. E. Flecker called 'The Golden Road to Samarkand'. Do you know where Samarkand is? Why was the road to it called 'Golden'?

5. What is 'The Blue Danube'? In what city was it written?

6. If the temperature of the bath-water was 150° F, would you feel inclined to get into it?

7. Sherry and port take their names from two towns in different countries. What are the towns, and in what countries are they?

8. What is the present capital of Western Germany? What was the capital of Germany before 1939?

9. What are the names given to instruments for measuring (a) the pressure of the atmosphere; (b) temperature; and (c) very small distances or angles?

10. What are Siamese twins? Why are they so called?

1. When and where do people go aquaplaning?

2. What is a parody? You may know the verse by Jane Taylor:

   > 'Twinkle, twinkle, little star,
   > How I wonder what you are!
   > Up above the world so high,
   > Like a diamond in the sky.'

   Do you know the parody of it in *Alice's Adventures In Wonderland*? Who spoke it in that book?

3. What is an off-licence?

4. What birds which are often kept as pets in this country can be taught to talk?

5. A poem by Sir Walter Scott begins:

   > 'Pibroch of Donuil Dhu,
   > Pibroch of Donuil.'

   Do you know what a pibroch is?

6. What are the meanings of 'a titfer'; 'going up the apples'; and 'take a butcher's round the back'? If these are too difficult, do you know what 'Rosie Lee' and 'plates of meat' stand for? These are five examples of the same sort of expression. What is it called?

7. If the sun at midday shone through the left-hand window of the train or car as you sat facing the front, in what direction would you be travelling?

8. Who was J. L. MacAdam? What English words come from his name?

9. What king was reigning in England when Columbus reached America?

10. Who has a tonsure? Where is it?

1. Who were the Merchant of Venice and the Moor of Venice?

2. What is there distinctive about the appearance of a magpie?

3. What is the significance of the phrases East End and West End?

4. What instrument is Yehudi Menuhin famous for playing?

5. If you are walking after dark along a country road which has no pavements, what precautions should you take?

6. What is the name of the most southerly of the United States on the Pacific coast?

7. When were the two occasions on which England was attacked by the plague? What animal was it that spread the disease?

8. What is required for a batsman to score six runs with one stroke at cricket?

9. If a gipsy asks you to cross her palm with silver, what does she want you to do? What will she do in return?

10. What word is it that has two meanings – a crushing reply, and a piece of apparatus used in the laboratory?

1. If a man was handling a spinnaker where would he be?

2. Earl Warren, Chief Justice of the United States, on 20 January 1969, administered the oath of office to a fourth President in succession. Who were the four?

3. Is it an offence against the law for a dog or a cat to be in the street without a collar bearing its owner's name and address?

4. There is a well-known song called 'The Road To The Isles'. What Isles are these? Where are they situated?

5. What sort of instrument is a Strad?

6. What do we call the things called sneakers in the U.S.A.?

7. What race takes place every year between Putney and Mortlake?

8. What is a monorail?

9. Salmonella is (a) a young salmon; (b) a type of bacteria; (c) a stew from Eastern Europe; or (d) a well-known pianist. Which is right?

10. Can you think of words all beginning with CON- and meaning (a) a policeman; (b) hollow; (c) the fruit of a

tree; (d) the American Houses of Parliament; (e) to defeat; (f) sweetmeats; (g) a musical performance; (h) to hide; (i) a kind of eel; and (j) a musical instrument?

1. What is a gymkhana? Has the word any connexion with gymnasium?

2. What is there unusual about the animal which is called a marsupial?

3. Can dogs swim naturally?

4. Has it ever been possible to walk from England to Europe? And from Ireland to Europe?

5. Can you think of ten words each of four letters that make other words when the letters are reversed? (For example, 'moor' becomes 'room' when it is put the other way round.)

6. What is the difference between haze, mist, and fog? What is sometimes said to be fogged?

7. Is it cooler to wear black or white clothes in a hot country? Why?

8. What is a monkey puzzle? Why has it been given this name?

9. What is a percussion instrument? How many such instruments can you think of?

10. Who was Polyphemus? What Greek hero came to his country? How did this hero escape?

1. Which side of the Pennine range in England is the wetter – the Lancashire side or the Yorkshire side? Is rain more likely in this country when the wind is in the east or in the west?

2. What is the significance of the letters R.S.V.P. on an invitation?

3. What is a siphon used for? What do you do to make it?

4. Is the long side of an ordinary English stamp more or less than one inch?

5. If an American said that he had a flat, what would he probably mean? (He would not be referring to where he lived.)

6. What is the purpose of ringing a bird? How is it done?

7. Who is 'in his hammock an' a thousand mile away'? And what is he doing?

8. In what part of the world is the olive still most commonly grown? What is the most important thing we get from its fruit?

9. Can you think of words each beginning with BUC- and being (a) the name of a European capital; (b) a pirate; (c) a male deer; (d) the name of an English county; and (e) a shoe or belt fastening?

10. What are the exact words of the chorus of 'Auld Lang Syne'?

1. What does the Colditz Story tell? Can you give the name of another similar story?

2. In what country were chop-sticks originally used?

3. What is the name of the Saint (the hero of the books by Leslie Charteris)?

4. What fairly common birds do people hope to attract to their gardens by hanging containers of nuts, at which the birds peck as they hang upside down?

5. Is the name of the island off the south coast of England correctly spelled as the Isle of White?

6. What sort of thing is a fuselage? What is it that has one?

7. For what book is Mrs Beeton famous?

8. What is stencilling?

9. Who was Prime Minister in 1965? And who in 1968?

10. What is margarine made from?

1. What is a mammoth? Where is one found? If you were to describe something as 'mammoth', what would you mean?

2. Where does the Queen go for her summer holidays?

3. With what exploit is William Tell connected in legend? In what country did he live?

4. Two-ply and four-ply – what is measured in this way?

5. Where are guy-ropes to be found? What is their purpose?

6.   John Marshall
   _____|_____
   Elizabeth Smith = Samuel   Mary = Alfred Bright
                 | |
              Charles   William

   (a) What are the surnames of Charles and William?
   (b) What relation are they to each other?
   (c) What relation are Elizabeth and Mary?
   (d) What relation is Charles to John Marshall?
   (e) What relation is Charles to Mary?

7. What do the well-known initials C.I.D. stand for? And what do the initials F.B.I. stand for?

8. What is a trunk call?

9. A poet wrote:

> 'Chimborazo, Cotopaxi,
> They have stolen my soul away.'

What are they?

10. Where do lions, springboks and wallabies play one another?

1. What is an anorak? The word does not look English; can you say from what language it comes?

2. By what sort of land is an oasis surrounded?

3. Can you fill in the blanks from the first part of a poem called 'The Months'?

> 'January brings the . . .
> Makes our feet and fingers glow.
> February brings the . . .
> Thaws the frozen . . . again.
> March brings . . . loud and shrill,
> Stirs the dancing . . .
> April brings the . . . sweet,
> Scatters . . . at our feet.
> May brings flocks of pretty lambs,
> Skipping by their fleecy . . .
> June brings tulips, lilies, . . .
> Fills the children's hands with posies.'

(The second half of the poem is question 9 in set 71.)

4. What are the highest ranks to which an officer can rise in the army, the navy and the air force?

5. Is the title of Shakespeare's play *A Midsummers Night Dream* correct?

6. Who was ruling in Rome when Jesus Christ was born, and who in England in the year 1900?

7. Where in England are there wild ponies?

8. The people of a certain race divide the world into Gentiles and themselves. Who are the people?

9. (a) Who turned into gold everything he touched? (b) Who sailed in the *Golden Hind*? (c) What is a golden wedding? (d) Who killed the goose that laid the golden eggs? (e) 'All that . . . is not gold.' What is the missing word in this proverb?

10. What use is made of the Cresta run? Where is it?

1. Which is the first floor of a building?

2. Which of the following flowers are killed off by the first real frost? – Chrysanthemum, dahlia, michaelmas daisy, nasturtium, rose.

3. What exploits did the Greeks say were carried out by Perseus?

4. What is the name of the square in the centre of Moscow? Many Russians visit the tomb of a famous man in this square. Who is it?

5. To what questions might these be the answers? – (a) $180°$; (b) $2\pi r$; (c) $\dfrac{bh}{2}$?

6. Can you give two completely different meanings of the word 'tattoo'?

7. What do you know about the character of the little girl who 'wore a little curl right down the middle of her forehead'?

8. What is a desert rat?

9. What was the Silver Ghost built by Henry Royce in 1906?

10. What are the three main political parties in this country? This may be an easy question, but can you say what are the two main parties in the United States?

60

1. Can you fill in the blanks in the following?

   'The rule of the road is a paradox quite,
       For as you are driving along,
       If you keep to the . . . you are sure to go . . .
       If you go to the . . . you are . . .'

2. What does a bench-mark look like? What does it indicate? Where might you be likely to see one?

3. If we say nowadays that a place is an inferno, we mean that it is blazing furiously. But how was the word first used?

4. Which of these cities are in Russia? – Belgrade, Budapest, Helsinki, Kiev, Riga, Warsaw.

5. What legends do you know of that are connected with Glastonbury in Somersetshire?

6. Is it true to say that men are descended from monkeys?

7. What is Alitalia?

8. Who wrote a story called 'The Ugly Duckling'? What did the Ugly Duckling turn out to be?

9. What proportion of the population of the world lives in China? Is it approximately $\frac{1}{10}$, $\frac{1}{5}$, $\frac{1}{4}$, or $\frac{1}{3}$?

10. If on a holiday you went through a lock, what sort of holiday would it probably be?

61

1. What is there illogical about the names of the months September, October, November, and December? Can you account for it?

2. What is haemorrhage?

3. What is the proper fuel to use at a barbecue?

4. What modern country has on its red flag the crescent moon and a star in white?

5. Can earwigs fly?

6. Near what great city is the Palace of Versailles? For what king was it built?

7. Can you fill in the missing letters to make the names of famous English poets? (One dot represents one letter.)
   (a) . . nn . . . n   (b) K . . t .   (c) C . . . c . r
   (d) . . lt . .   (e) W . r . sw . . . .

8. Where do the Cossacks live? For what ability are they noted?

9. There are two men named John about whom we read in the Gospels. What is each of them known for?

10. What part of an army is the vanguard? What is the opposite called?

1. Do oak trees have flowers?

2. How did the books in the Bible called Genesis and Exodus get their names?

3. What royal castle is situated on the river Thames upstream of London? And what famous public school is close to it?

4. Who wrote the book called *Gulliver's Travels*? Gulliver visited countries called Lilliput and Brobdingnag. What sort of people lived in them?

5. What are flying saucers?

6. Is it true that Jamaica is one of the islands of the East Indies?

7. If a man was having trouble in a bunker what sort of man would he probably be?

8. Are there issues of postage stamps specially for the Channel Islands and the Isle of Man?

9. In what sort of country is a cable car used?

10. Can you fill in the blanks in the following expressions with the names of places in England? – (a) To carry coals to ... (b) To send to ... (c) To set the ... on fire. (d) To grin like a ... cat.

1. In what countries are Aberdeen and Aberystwyth? Why are there many names beginning with 'Aber' in certain parts of Britain?

2. What is the colour of a postman's uniform?

3. What is supposed to have happened to the Princes in the Tower? Is the story true?

4. Where do you see riding-lights?

5. Why are babies given rose-hip or blackcurrant syrup?

6. What is the meaning of the word 'quick' in the phrase 'the quick and the dead'? Do you know of any other phrases in which 'quick' has this meaning?

7. How does a spiral staircase differ from an ordinary one?

8. What game begins with the call of 'Play'? And what begins with a bully-off?

9. What well-known photographer has married into the royal family?

10. To what questions are the following the answers? (They refer to the same man.) (a) On the feast of Stephen. (b) A poor man gathering fuel.

1. Where is the great wall that was built to guard Britain from attack by the barbarians? Who had it built? Do you know of any other country that was guarded in a similar way?

2. What did the Beast do to Beauty? What did Beauty do to the Beast?

3. What was meant by 'walking the plank'? Who had to do it?

4. Which breed of cow produces milk with the highest percentage of butterfat – Friesian, Jersey, or Shorthorn?

5. On what canals are the towns of Port Said and Colon situated?

6. What sort of person is commonly referred to as a back-seat driver?

7. What do the initials B.B.C. stand for?

8. Where is the famous church of St Martin's in The Fields?

9. What was a blunderbuss?

10. If you wanted to find a razor-shell, where would you look for it?

1. How are zebra crossings indicated? Who has the right of way on one of them -- a pedestrian or a motorist?

2. Who was the husband of Eve? Where was their first home? What did she persuade him to do? How were they punished for this?

3. Who flew the Jolly Roger?

4. What English bird makes a noise that sounds like the bath-water running away? (It is the wife of a bird with an extremely well-known note.)

5. Can you give the names of five large cities (or towns) in England that begin with the letter L?

6. What is chop suey? With what country do you connect it?

7. The following are definitions of various kinds of places in which people live. Can you give the name of each of them? – (a) A house with only one storey. (b) A residence that occupies one floor of a building. (c) A large building fortified for defence. (d) A hut made of snow in which Eskimos live. (e) A house on wheels nowadays often towed behind a car.

8. What is Belle Vue? What is Whipsnade?

9. Who wrote a story about the Elephant's Child? What was his great fault?

10. A family were walking in the country on a sunny summer's day. They had with them some food and a compass. They had agreed to walk across the open countryside, and have lunch at one o'clock. They had no watch, clock, or radio with them, and they met no one. How did they know when it was lunchtime?

1. Is it ever permissible to overtake a vehicle in this country by passing it on the left?

2. What was 'the Chief Defect of Henry King'? What happened to him because of it?

3. How is the word *sumach* pronounced? What is it? Where was it originally to be found? Do you know anything interesting about it?

4. Against what king of England did Hereward the Wake fight? Who wrote a book about Hereward? What does Wake mean?

5. If you had a television set, a fixed radio set and a portable radio, how many licences would you need?

6. If you strike an octave on the piano how many white notes are there between the two that you touch? Do you know the meaning of the word *octave*?

7. What is Eurovision?

8. Can you give the two different meanings that the word *sleeper* has for railwaymen?

9. What is the difference between geography and geology?

10. Hinduism is one of the great religions of the world. Where do most Hindus live?

1. At some busy road junctions, where there are traffic lights, vehicles wishing to turn right are routed in this way. What is the purpose of it?

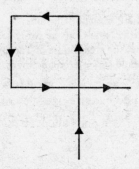

2. In what district is Chatsworth situated? Who owns it?

3. What is the usual purpose for which privet is grown in this country? Do you know of any other plants which are used for the same purpose?

4. What is the first thing that should be done if a person is found suffering from electric shock?

5. You have probably seen ITV programmes by Granada and know its headquarters are in Manchester. But do you know in what country there is a province called Granada?

6. What do we mean if we say that something is a white elephant?

7. For what purpose does a man make his will?

8. What sport is governed by the Queensberry Rules?

9. Can you give the names of five of the planets that move round the sun?

10.

> 'Lars Porsena of Clusium
> By the Nine Gods he swore
> That the great house of Tarquin
> Should suffer wrong no more.'

(a) Of what country was Lars Porsena the ruler? (b) What city did he attack as is described in the poem that begins above? (c) What prevented him from capturing the city?

1. What was seen by the Magi, or the Three Wise Men? Where did it lead them? What gifts did they take with them?

2. Why do we often shiver when we become cold?

3. Which of the following are foods? – Alibi, lapis lazuli, ravioli, scampi, spermaceti. Do you know what sort of thing each food is, and what the non-foods are?

4. (a) What man took his seat in the House of Commons in 1833 and made his last speech there in 1894? (b) And what man first became a member in 1900 and made his last appearance there in 1964?

5. Many taps in houses have the colour red or blue on them. Which colour goes on which tap?

6. You know that the Stone Ages were so called because tools and weapons were made out of stone. What kind of stone was almost always used?

7. What is the difference between an amateur and a professional in sport?

8. What do you know about Galileo?

9. How many lamps must be carried on a bicycle at night? What besides a lamp must be fitted to enable the cycle to be seen from the rear?

10. What is a torpedo?

1. Does the shade temperature in England ever reach 90° F? Does it ever reach 100° F?

2. (a) Windermere in the Lake District is on the border where two counties join. What are they? (b) What two counties are separated by the river Tees?

3. Who were the Amazons? Have they any connexion with the river Amazon? How do we use the word Amazon today?

4. What show sometimes takes place in September at Farnborough, and what show takes place in Olympia at the end of October?

5. What is the score if each player has gained one point in a game of tennis?

6. What does Big Ben tell us?

7. What part of a house are the eaves? What is eaves-dropping?

8. What is a lullaby? One of the best known of lullabies begins 'Hush-a-bye, baby, on the tree top'. Can you give the other three lines?

9. The word 'maroon' has several completely different meanings. Can you say what three of them are?

10. Can you describe the shape and colour of a ladybird? Is it an insect or what? Can you give a rhyme connected with this creature?

1. Which is the fastest of the ordinary strokes used in swimming?

2. Are polar bears found only in the Arctic regions, only in the Antarctic regions, or in both? And what about penguins?

3. John Masefield wrote a poem about 'the old bold mate of Henry Morgan'. Who was Henry Morgan?

4. Why do people go to Lourdes? With what person in particular is the place connected?

5. Is it true that the river Volga flows into the Black Sea and the Danube into the Mediterranean?

6. If a person who has committed a serious crime in Britain escapes to another country, can he be arrested there and brought back here for trial?

7. How often is a General Election held in this country?

8. Is Mozart famous as a painter, an architect, a composer or a sculptor?

9. Can you complete the following expressions? – (a) Through . . . and thin; (b) To go at something . . . and tongs; (c) To play fast and . . .; (d) To fight . . . and nail; (e) . . . and starts.

10. There are two kinds of evening-dress worn by men at formal dinners. Can you describe how they differ from each other?

1. What is the purpose of an insulator?

2. What is a yashmak? If you were wearing one in what part of the world would you probably be?

3. Where is chlorophyll to be found?

4. Can you put these towns – Buenos Aires, Chicago, Lyons, Milan, Yokohama – into the right countries – Argentina, France, Italy, Japan, the United States?

5. You know what a fan club is. But do you know what word 'fan' is short for?

6. What is the name given to writing of this sort?

7. Why do many Scottish names begin with Mac (or Mc or M'), and many Irish names with O'? Do you know other affixes that form personal names with the same meaning?

8. Can you arrange these periods of prehistory in the order in which they occurred? – Bronze Age, Iron Age, Old Stone Age, New Stone Age.

9. Question 3 of set 58 gave you the first half of 'The Months'. Can you fill in the blanks in the second half?

Hot July brings cooling . . .
Apricots and gilly . . .
August brings the . . . of . . .
Then the harvest home is borne.
Warm September brings the . . .
. . . then begin to shoot.
Fresh October brings the . . .
Then to gather . . . is pleasant.
Dull November brings the . . .
Then the . . . are whirling fast.
Chill December brings the . . .
. . . fire and Christmas treat.'

10. You know the meaning of the abbreviations £ s d, but do you know how these letters came to stand for pounds, shillings and pence?

1. We sometimes talk about people 'swimming the Channel'. What Channel is it that they swim? Who was the first man to swim it?

2. There are many words in English that begin with tele-. Can you give five of them all completely different? And do you know the meaning of the prefix?

3. Some parts of the world are subject to tremendous storms, which are called by various names. How many of these names do you know?

4. What is a brace and bit used for?

5. With what do you associate Kew? At what time of the year does the poet tell us 'to go down to Kew'?

6. A man wanted to dry out an under-the-stairs cupboard, which was brick built with an airtight door and no ventilation. He put a lighted paraffin stove, completely filled with fuel, in the cupboard and closed the door. Why did he find when he opened the door two hours later that the heater was out?

7. Can you complete the verse of the hymn that begins –

   'All things bright and beautiful'?

8. In many parts of England some villages have names of two words like Ashton Keynes. What is the usual reason for this?

9. 'Of his bones is coral made', sang Ariel in 'The Tempest'. What is coral properly made of? Where is it to be found?

10. What sort of clothes are worn by the conductor of a great orchestra in the concert hall?

1. Mortar and putty are both used for joining things together. What things?

2. This is an old question, which perhaps you haven't heard. Three men set out to walk to Dundee, Dundalk, and Dunkirk. If they all walked at the same pace, which one arrived first at his destination?

3. What is meant by 'burying the hatchet'? What people had this custom? What other phrase with much the same meaning have we got from these same people?

4. Why was the Wandering Jew supposed to be condemned to wander about until the end of the world? In Coleridge's poem 'The Ancient Mariner', the mariner is given a similar punishment. What had he done to deserve it?

5. With what sports do you connect Epsom Downs, Lord's, St Andrew's, Twickenham, and Wimbledon?

6. What was the fate of Pompeii?

7. What are the names of the two Houses of Parliament in this country? In what part of London are they situated?

8. Where and when would you expect to see gossamer? How is it produced?

9. Who was usually supposed to have written the Psalms? He has been called 'the sweet singer of the house of Israel'.

10. What is a fox trot?

1. Is cotton-wool cotton or wool? Is bees-wax made by bees?

2. Do we hear the thunder before the flash of lightning, or the other way round? Can you give a reason for your answer?

3. What was used for writing on by the people who lived in Babylon and in ancient Egypt?

4. Can you think of words all beginning with COL- and meaning (a) a breaking down; (b) an associate; (c) a place of learning; (d) a mark of punctuation; (e) an army officer; and (f) to dash together.

5. If one man brings a lawsuit against another, which of them is called the defendant? What is the other person called?

6. Is it true that there are regular aeroplane routes over the North Pole?

7. Which is the intruder in the following sets?
   (a) Pike, carp, trout, mackerel.
   (b) Oak, fir, sycamore, beech.
   (c) Ayr, Fife, Sutherland, Tyrone.

8. Tom is the hero of *The Water-Babies* by Charles Kingsley. What was the name of his master? What did his master make him do?

9. What country is famous for tulips, windmills and canals?

10. Who were Roland and Oliver? What is meant by giving a Roland for an Oliver?

1. What are the names given to the people who (a) design and plan buildings; (b) make statues; and (c) write plays?

2. Are the Maldives (a) a disease; (b) ingredients of a salad; (c) a group of islands; or (d) armour worn in the Middle Ages?

3. What is pewter? What is, or was, it used for?

4. What great change in world opinion was started by Martin Luther?

5. What is a protractor used for? What is its shape?

6. In a match one boys' team beat its opponents by two to one. What game was probably being played?

7. How many great-grandparents does every person have, dead or alive? And how many great great grand-parents?

8. If a joint of your body is dislocated, what have you done? If a hand is amputated, what happens?

9. What is the chief difference between a monarchy and a republic?

10. Can you think of the groups of four items each to which the following belong?
    (a) Mopsy, Cottontail.
    (b) Clubs, spades.
    (c) George III, Victoria.

1. What are the meanings of the phrases *viva voce*, *sotto voce*, and *vice versa*?

2. Can you complete the group of seven which contains Kent and Northumbria? What is the group?

3. What sort of vehicle shows on top of the body (a) a flashing blue light; and (b) a flashing red light?

4. You are in a barber's shop sitting facing a mirror on the back wall. On the window there is a transparent advertisement facing outwards. Would you see the advertisement forwards or backwards in the mirror?

5. How many sets of twelve can you think of? (For example, if the number was ten one of the answers might be 'the ten commandments'.)

6. What is the proper meaning of the word 'camouflage' When was it first used on a large scale? Why was it necessary?

7. What, according to Edward Lear, were the peculiarities in the appearance of the Pobble and the Dong?

8. Woodworkers talk about hard and soft woods. From what kinds of trees do we get these two kinds of wood?

9. What is meant by 'starting from scratch' and by 'scratching from a race'?

10. Do you know why America is so called? Why were the original inhabitants called Indians?

1. What happens when an animal or a bird moults?

2. What is meant by doing the hat trick? Have you any idea how the phrase came into existence?

3. Who wrote the poems called *The Canterbury Tales*? How did they get their name? Why did pilgrims go to Canterbury?

4. There is an airport named after Leonardo da Vinci. In what country would you expect it to be? Why does it seem especially appropriate to name an airport after him?

5. Are there any cars, vans or lorries on the roads today which are powered by electricity and do not use petrol or diesel oil at all?

6. Do Canadians reckon their money in pounds, shillings and pence as we do?

7. Where and what was Gethsemane? What happened there?

8. (a) What is the largest town in Northumberland? (b) What town is on the border between Northumberland and Scotland? (c) What is the port on the river Humber? (d) What resemblance is there between the names of these towns?

9. Is there anything wrong with this sentence: 'The music rose to a crescendo'? How is the last word pronounced?

10. In Westerns the sheriff is usually an important charac-
    ter. What exactly are his duties ? In the Middle Ages in
    England also the sheriff was important. What did he
    do then ?

1. Is Pythagoras famous as a sculptor, a mathematician, a general or an explorer?

2. What person connected with the Church of England wears gaiters?

3. What is meant by 'blazing the trail'? Can you think of another use in which 'blaze' has much the same meaning?

4. How many towns in Great Britain can you think of that end in -SEA?

5. What part of a ship might you say corresponds to the window of a house?

6. Sir W. S. Gilbert wrote the words for some famous comic operas. What are these operas called? Can you give the titles of two of them? Who wrote the music?

7. What country borders France for part of the way on the south? And what sea forms the rest of the southern boundary?

8. The following sentence is from an American advertisement. How can you tell this? 'Fiberglass is tough and extremely strong, corrosion-resistant and easy to mold'.

9. If you were making a round trip what would you be doing?

10. What happens if a small balloon, sealed but not inflated, is put under a bell-jar, which is then emptied of air?

1. Are seals mammals or fish? Are they to be found anywhere on the coasts of Great Britain?

2. In what game are the Ashes played for? What teams compete for them?

3. What is a palette? Who uses it? What for?

4. What is meant by working one's passage?

5. Can you finish these book titles? – (a) Anne of Green ... (b) The Flight of the ... (c) Girl of the ... (d) Under the Red ...

6. Has there ever been a woman Prime Minister of Great Britain?

7. What is the name of the range of mountains that may be called the centre of Europe?

8.
> '... was a citizen
> Of credit and renown,
> A train-band captain eke was he
> Of famous London town.'

Who is being referred to here? What exploit is recounted in the poem that begins in this way?

9. Is it true that the *Messiah* was composed by Handel?

10. Can you complete this sentence? In 1215 King John put his seal to ... on the island of ... in the river ...

1. What is the reason for a man going bankrupt?

2. Where is there a district called the Elephant and Castle? And in what cities are there streets called Broadway and Pennsylvania Avenue?

3. In what way do safety belts help to reduce injuries in a car accident?

4. In what sort of country do cacti grow?

5. What is the lowest age at which a boy or girl in this country can at present leave school?

6. In what country and at what period was a toga worn?

7. What is hogmanay? What is haggis? (If you come from a certain part of Britain you may find this an easy question.)

8.

> 'The king sits in Dunfermline toun,
> Drinking the blude-red wine.'

What did he order one of his sea-captains to do? What was the seaman's name?

9. What is meant by 'kicking into touch'?

10. Susan and Sam are in a mathematically-minded family. They are twins. If Susan has twice as many brothers as sisters, and Sam has the same number of brothers as sisters, how many boys and how many girls are there in the family?

1. What kind of rock is it that forms the white cliffs of Dover and lies under the turf of the Downs, Salisbury Plain and other English hills?

2. Can you give a description of a unicorn? Has there ever been a creature like it?

3. What famous events in the history of this country happened in 55 B.C., 1415, 1485, and 1945?

4. What is meant by the draught of a boat? Why must it be known to the person navigating?

5. Who was 'bred en bawn in a brier-patch'? Who told stories about him?

6. Can you fill in the blanks? Christians worship in a . . . Jews in a . . . and Mohammedans in a . . .

7. If someone's watch is actually 5 minutes slow, although he thinks it is 10 minutes fast, what will happen if he uses his watch to see that he gets to the station with 10 minutes to spare before his train goes?

8. What counties adjoin Cornwall?

9. Are there any people on the earth who see the sun in the north?

10. What is observed in an observatory?

1. In what sort of place does the willow grow? What thing used by schoolboys and (grownups as well) is made from willow?

2. What connexion is there between the items in the groups which follow?
   (a) The Old Curiosity Shop, David Copperfield, Great Expectations.
   (b) E. Nesbit, Hugh Lofting, Alison Uttley.
   (c) Babar, Orlando, White Fang.

3. Which of the following mountains are active volcanoes? – Etna, Fujiyama, Hecla, the Jungfrau, Popocatepetl, Vesuvius.

4. Why is an unmarried woman called a spinster?

5. What event has taken place at four-year intervals in these cities since the war? One city is omitted; can you say what it is? –
   London, Helsinki, Melbourne, Tokio, Mexico City.

6. Who is the only person who can be made the Prince of Wales? Is there a Prince of Wales at the present time?

7. What was the religion of this country during the Middle Ages (say from 1000 to 1400)?

8. A number of wild animals belong to the cat family. Can you give the names of some of them?

9. Which ends of a ship are the bow and the stern?

10. If you add together half a pair, half a dozen, half a score, half a century, and half a gross, how much do you get?

1. Who is being described in this passage? What is the occasion?
'A skinny young man only just leaving boyhood behind, something above middle height, with feet whose adolescent proportions to his size were accentuated by the thinness of his legs and his big half-boots ... The newcomer was dressed in a badly-fitting uniform which was soaked right through by the spray; a skinny neck stuck out of the high stock, and above the neck was a white bony face.'

2. Where can you see bishops, knights and castles close together?

3. What revolutions began in 1789 and 1917?

4. Of what Christian names are these abbreviations? – Connie, Jim, Molly, Peggy, Penny, Ted.

5. In what general direction is the Thames flowing when it goes through London?

6. If a car carries a plate with the letters GB on it, what does it signify?

7. What is 'early to bed and early to rise' said to make a man?

8. What are the various names given in this country to men who have been ordained?

9. Of what plants do we eat the leaves?

10. What are the insects that fly about in great swarms in certain hot countries, settle on the vegetation and do a great deal of damage to it?

1. Is there such a thing as a mermaid? What form is it supposed to have? What is the meaning of the first part of the word?

2. Do you know the way in which the word *blitz* came to have its present meaning in English?

3. Who met the Mad Hatter, the March Hare and the Dormouse all at the same time? What was the occasion?

4. From what European languages are those spoken in South America mostly derived?

5. On what part of the body did Queen Elizabeth I wear her ruff? And a nun her wimple?

6. What other name do you know for 'Old Glory'?

7. (a) What chemical substance is kept in water and catches fire when it is taken out?
   (b) If a little of a certain domestic substance is put at the back of a light paper boat, the boat will move through the water. What is this substance?

8. Why do we break eggs separately into a cup before mixing them together?

9. Is any player allowed to kick the ball at hockey?

10. Can you pair off the towns in A with the items in B? –
    A. Blackpool, Durham, London, Plymouth, Rugby.
    B. Cathedral, the Hoe, School, the Strand, Tower.

1. What is a jay? What is a jay-walker?

2. Is there a capital of Asia?

3. What are the names of the persons who carry out these jobs? – (a) Mending water pipes in a house. (b) Being in charge of a large collection of books. (c) Loading and unloading ships. (d) Collecting fares on a bus.

4. Where are groynes to be found? What are they there for? What effect of them can be seen?

5. During the Middle Ages kings and noblemen often kept falcons. What were they used for?

6. What part of the world do we call the Orient? What is its opposite?

7. Budgerigars often have something hung in their cages as a delicacy. What is it?

8. What persons in nursery rhymes and stories are connected with a hungry dog, a cow in the corn, Banbury Cross, a little lamb, and frogs and snails and puppy dogs' tails?

9. Are more boy babies born in this country than girl babies?

10. What is an optical illusion?

1. *Homer* is a word which has two completely different meanings. Do you know what they are?

2. Has Sussex a sea-board on the east or south coast?

3. There is a famous picture of sunflowers. Was it painted by Gauguin, Picasso, Renoir, or Van Gogh?

4. Who was reigning in this country when you were born?

5. From what animals do we get chops and steaks?

6. If you had to send an important message very quickly to someone a hundred miles away, what methods might you use? What are the limitations of these methods?

7. In some games people talk about 'winning the rubber'. What is the meaning of this phrase?

8. What is marquetry? What is a marquis? What is a marquee?

9. How can one tell the age of a tree?

10. Which of these drinks, taken in excess, would make a person drunk? Beer, champagne, cider, lemon barley water, rum, sherry, soda water, tonic water, vodka, whisky.

1. What is meant by (a) heaping coals of fire on some-body's head; (b) taking the lion's share; (c) holding out the olive branch?

2. What is the meaning of the name Cape Finisterre? Can you think of the name of another Cape that has the same meaning?

3. What is measured in hands?

4. Two knights had served their Lord nobly. 'As a reward,' he said, 'you may choose either one payment only of £3,000, or monthly payments for a year starting with £1 and doubling each month.' Sir Prudent chose the monthly payments. 'Thou art a fool,' whispered Sir Grasper, as he went out chuckling with his £3,000. Who received the larger amount?

5. In the Psalms we read that 'the days of our age' are so many, and though nowadays many people live much longer, this is still regarded as a good old age. What is it?

6. Are there postal deliveries on Boxing Day and Good Friday?

7. What are cigars made of?

8. What disease is spread by the bite of mosquitoes? Where do mosquitoes breed?

9. Is it true that (a) worms are bad for the garden; and (b) all garden rubbish is best burnt?

10. Where is Anne Hathaway's cottage? Why do thousands of people visit it every year?

1. What is the best-known story connected with Noah?

2. Can you fill in the gaps in the following words to make the names of well-known flowers? – (a) . . nsy; (b) del . . . . . . m; (c) na . . . . m; (d) h . . . . h . . k; (e) mar . . . . d.

3. What is there at Cape Kennedy?

4. Which of these animals are found wild in Great Britain? – Beaver, badger, deer, fox, wolf.

5. Can you draw the sign which indicates a garage that tests for roadworthiness cars over a certain age?

6. What events make up the pentathlon? Do you know the name of any similar contest?

7. What compound often prepared in school laboratories is commonly said to have a smell like that of rotten eggs?

8. In this country we eat bread and potatoes to give bulk to our diet. What takes the place of these foods in many eastern countries?

9. Are these seaside towns on the north, east, west, or south coasts of England? – Blackpool, Bournemouth, Brighton, Scarborough, Torquay, Great Yarmouth.

10. 'Here comes the . . . that must be caught with tickling', says somebody in 'Twelfth Night'. What kind of fish can be caught with tickling? What character in the play is referred to?

1. What is a grass widow (or widower)? What sort of person is (or was) called a wallflower?

2. Where do the Maoris live?

3. What great historical event is shown in the pictures on the Bayeux Tapestry?

4. What is a photo-finish?

5. When things are inflated they frequently become warm. Can you think of anything that becomes cooler when the opposite happens?

6. Are the following works novels, plays or poems? – *Oliver Twist*, *Peter Pan*, *Kubla Khan*, *Silas Marner*, *Under Milk Wood*, *Waiting for Godot*.

7. Is it true that a man has travelled at 1,500 m.p.h. in the air?

8. For what reason does a man insure his house?

9. The following towns can be arranged in pairs which are fairly close to one another: Bradford, Chesterfield, Ipswich, Leeds, Liverpool, Manchester, Norwich, Portsmouth, Sheffield, Southampton. Can you pair them off?

10. What is an Old Master?

1. Where was the great iron-working district of England in the Middle Ages? Why was it there?

2. Can you name four important countries besides Great Britain and Ireland where English is spoken by most of the inhabitants as their first language?

3. Is it safe to drink water straight from (a) a river; (b) a small stream; or (c) a spring?

4. Can you fill in the blanks in the following? – Cinderella was badly treated by her . . . . She went to a ball in a coach made out of a . . .; at the ball she met a . . ., but she had to leave before the stroke of . . . . In her hurry she lost one of her tiny . . . made of . . .

5. What is Brasilia?

6. In what chapel does the Festival of Nine Lessons and Carols take place every Christmas Eve?

7. What was the Colossus of Rhodes? What modern English words come from this name?

8. (a) Who became Prime Minister of England on 10 May 1940; and (b) who on 16 October 1964?

9. ''Twas the sound of his horn called me from my bed,
   And the cry of his hounds has me oft-times led.'

   Who is the huntsman referred to in this well-known song? Where did he live?

10. Which of these metals can be magnetized – gold, copper, steel?

1. What is there about Helen Keller that makes her life-
   story so amazing?

2. Who is it that puts the crown on the sovereign's head
   at the coronation? In what building does the ceremony
   take place?

3. Which of these words rhyme? – Beard, bird, cared,
   feared, furred, heard, weird, whirred, word.

4. What is a vintage car? What is the original meaning
   of vintage?

5. What people used boomerangs? What is there unusual
   about these weapons?

6. If we call somebody a Hercules what do we mean?
   And if we call somebody a Solomon? How have these
   meanings arisen?

7. What is the name of the Owl of the Remove at Grey-
   friars School?

8. Can you think of the name of two plants (or trees)
   that begin with *horse*?

9. In what parts of the body are the fibula and the tibia?

10. To what countries would you go for holidays on the
    Costa Brava or the Riviera, or in the fjords or the
    Trossachs?

1. Of what countries are the daffodil, the rose, the shamrock and the thistle the emblems?

2. At one time herds of many millions of buffalo (or bison) roamed about the plains. Where did they live?

3. What is the resemblance between Canberra, Ottawa, and Wellington?

4. Can you explain clearly the difference between speed and acceleration?

5. At sports meetings is there ever an event like the children's Hop, Skip, and Jump?

6. Which of these metals rust? – Brass, copper, gold, iron, silver, tin.

7. Who is the central figure in Dickens's story *The Christmas Carol*? What spirits appeared to him?

8. Who popularized the Promenade Concerts that are held in London every year? What are they generally called?

9. From what serious physical disabilities did Milton and Beethoven suffer?

10. Can you complete the phrase 'to discuss the pros and ...'? What does it mean?

1. In England when we meet a friend we may say 'Good morning'. What do French people say?

2. In what country did the Kaiser rule? From whose name is the title Kaiser derived?

3. Is there any ordinary four-wheeled car frequently seen in this country which has an overall length of less than ten feet?

4. What are Hengist and Horsa supposed to have done?

5. What part of the plant is the tomato we eat? And what is rhubarb?

6. What is a trident? Who are usually represented as holding one?

7. In what areas of this country are Dunkery Beacon and Kinder Scout to be found?

8. How do human beings form gates and houses?

9. Are these the heads of their respective countries? – Emir, emperor, king, president, prime minister, sultan, vizier?

10. Is it true that the English pint is bigger than the American pint?

1. What bird is referred to in the line 'The slant-legged ... with autumn on his chest'? What is meant by 'autumn on his chest'?

2. If you were on a slimming diet which of these foods would you cut down on? – apples, bread, brussels sprouts, cereals, chipped potatoes, chocolate, cheese, eggs, fish, meat, sugar.

3. What are bricks made of? What is meant by the phrase 'Making bricks without straw'? Who were the people who were ordered to do this?

4. Which is the larger in each of the following pairs of countries? Which has the larger population? – (a) Canada or Great Britain; (b) Greece or Italy; (c) France or the U.S.S.R.

5. Where did the Pilgrim Fathers go to?

6. With what do you connect Real Madrid?

7. (a) What is the name given to the lines on a map that pass through the points that are the same height above sea level? (b) And what to those lines that connect places having equal temperatures?

8. In what part of England did the Danes chiefly settle? We can often tell because the names of many of the towns and villages have one of two endings. What are these?

9. You have two bricks, a jar filled with water and a piece of ordinary writing paper (8 in. × 6 in.) or bigger. Is there any way in which you can support the jar of water so that it is resting on the middle of the paper while the ends of the paper are supported by the two bricks?

10. What is the purpose of the valve on a bicycle tyre? How does it work? Where do we find valves in the human body?

1. Who was it that designed St Paul's Cathedral in London? What is the name of the hill that leads up to it?

2. What is a hydrofoil? What is a hovercraft?

3. After what period can this country properly be called England? What was its name earlier?

4. Are sponges animal, vegetable, or mineral?

5. Can you give the names of the various continents in the world?

6. Why were the Iron Age men able to defeat men with weapons of bronze? And why were the Bronze Age men able to defeat the Stone Age men?

7. What is an ostrich supposed to do when it thinks it is in danger?

8. *Aqua* is the Latin for water. How many English words can you think of beginning with aqua-? What is the connexion of each of them with water?

9. What is meant by the phrase 'First XI *v* the Rest'?

10.
   'By thirty hills I hurry down,
   Or slip between the ridges,
   By twenty thorps, a little town,
   And half a hundred bridges.'

Who is supposed to be speaking? Where does the speaker finish? Who wrote the poem?

1. In what city are Harlem and Manhattan?

2. What is lava? And what is a larva?

3. What is the approximate cost of a gallon of petrol in this country? How much petrol does the fuel tank of a car hold?

4. Which of the following flowers have a strong scent? — Carnation, dahlia, lily of the valley, lupin, rose, sunflower.

5. In the fairy tale how did the Princess show that she was 'A Real Princess'?

6. What have all these in common: snow in summer, a yellow flag, rest harrow, dog's mercury and lady's slipper?

7. What is meant by something being in the offing? What is making a landfall?

8. Are there any Eskimos living in northern Europe?

9. Do aeroplanes carry lights at night?

10. If you ordered breakfast in a French hotel what would you be given? What do the French call the meal that corresponds to our tea?

1. Pick out the item that does not fit in each of the following groups:
   (a) Two, three, four, five.
   (b) Cricket, football, hockey, golf.
   (c) Dickens, H. G. Wells, Keats, Thackeray.

2. Which of the following places are north and which south of the equator? – Bombay, Buenos Aires, Cairo, Cape Town, Sydney.

3. On some football grounds there are mounds for spectators called Spion Kop. How did these get the name?

4. Can you think of a railway terminus in Great Britain that is on an island which lies off another island (not Great Britain itself)?

5. Where can you see keys flying through the air?

6. Is J. M. W. Turner famous as an architect, a dramatist, a painter, or a musician?

7. What vehicles can go on the roads of this country without needing a number plate?

8. Between what towns did Watling Street run?

9. What is done in a hospital if the doctor wants to find out whether a patient has a slight fracture of a bone?

10. What is Barts? What is Bart short for?

1. In what British lake is there said to live a huge creature that no one has seen for certain?

2. Black, Red, White, Yellow – what word (not colour) can be added to each of these to put them all in the same group?

3. Where is peat found? What are its chief uses?

4. (a) Is it an offence for a cyclist to hold on to a moving vehicle in order to get a tow? (b) Is it to let a second person ride on the cycle, on the frame or step?

5. Can you give the exact forms of the phrases of which B.C., A.D., a.m., and p.m. are abbreviations? What are their meanings?

6. Who killed Cock Robin and who saw him die?

7. What is the approximate direction in which an aeroplane flies direct from London to Paris?

8. What is a possum? If you were playing possum what would you be doing?

9. What king of Scotland in 1603 became also king of England? What is the name of his mother?

10. Are there English newspapers called *The Daily Times*, the *Daily Telegraph* and the *Daily News*?

1. What is 99 in Roman numerals?

2. Of what countries are these ports? – Alexandria, Calcutta, Durban, Rio de Janeiro, Haifa.

3. What is the month of hay-making? What adjective is applied to it, often very inappropriately?

4. Do you think that Greenland is a suitable name for the country which is so called?

5. What are the names we give to the people who sell the following things? – (a) Vegetables, fruit and flowers. (b) Newspapers and periodicals. (c) Tea, sugar, cheese, bacon, etc. (d) Bread and cakes. (e) Meat.

6. Where is Cook Strait? If you do not know, the exploits of the man after whom it is named may give you a clue.

7. What are the two rather different meanings of the word *garage*? What is the word connected with an aeroplane that has a similar meaning to one of these?

8. In what parts of the world are there districts called the bush, the pampas, the savannahs, the tundra and the veld?

9. What is the Derby? What is meant by the expression 'a local Derby'?

10. Can you fill in the gaps in the following? – In 1825 what is usually regarded as the first railway was opened between . . . and . . . . In 1830 there was opened another between . . . and . . . ; on it ran the engine called the . . . built by . . . .

1. This is the hundredth and last set of questions; so here are some questions about 'hundred'. (a) How many pounds are there in a hundredweight? (b) Between what countries was the Hundred Years' War fought? (c) What are hundreds and thousands? (d) What is the Old Hundredth? (e) In what game is the expression 'a hundred up' used?

2. What is plywood?

3. Where do Trooping the Colour and Changing the Guard take place? When?

4. What did people sit on in the Middle Ages?

5. If there was a notice outside a hall 'Eyes Down 7.45', what would start at that time?

6. Is it true that Columbia, Minnesota and Saskatchewan are all in the United States of America?

7. Of what English counties are the Isle of Man and the Isle of Wight regarded as parts?

8. (a) In what year did the Armada set sail against England? (b) What king sent it? (c) In what country did he reign? (d) Who is the most famous Englishman that fought against the Armada?

9. Shopkeepers talk about their customers. How would a doctor, a lawyer, a hotel-keeper and a railway station-master refer to their 'customers'?

10. When is the Last Post sounded?

ANSWERS

1.   (a) is another man's poison.
    (b) does not make a summer.
    (c) deserves another.

2. Archers and foresters in the Middle Ages, in particular Robin Hood and his Merry Men.

3. You would see the Crown Jewels in the Tower of London, where you might also see one or two ravens.

4. Steam is invisible. What he saw was the cloud of condensed water (very small drops of water) that had formed as the steam cooled. If you look at a boiling kettle, you will see a space next to the spout before the cloud of water vapour forms; in this space is the steam.

5. A pun.

6. 'Dr Livingstone, I presume!' H. M. Stanley greeted Dr Livingstone like this at Ujiji in 1871.

7. Monastery, abbey, priory, convent, nunnery – there are five such names.

8. The lark.

9. '. . . the whole world, and lose his own soul?' (St Mark, viii, 36).

10. Only 1960 and 2000. A year is a leap year if its number is divisible by 4, e.g. 1960, but a beginning year of a century is only a leap year if it is divisible by 400, e.g. 2000.

1. Knossos was in the island of Crete; the king was called Minos; the monster was the Minotaur, who lived in a labyrinth and was killed by Theseus.

2. China and Wales have dragons for their symbols. The most famous man to kill a dragon is St George, the patron saint of England.

3. Violin, viola, cello, double-bass.

4. The snowdrop is the 'February fair-maid', although the flower is often later than that in the north.

5. The Big Top is the great tent which is erected for the performances of a touring circus. The big end is the larger end of the connecting rod in a car engine.

6. You would add the numbers together and divide the total by five.

7. The danger from shock.

8. It is a golfing expression used by golfers when, as happens occasionally, the drive or first shot sends the ball into the hole.

9. Coal.

10. Cardiff, Glasgow, Llandudno.

3

1. From maize, or Indian corn.

2. Wales. You would go north-west.

3. *Lorna Doone* by R. D. Blackmore.

4. Sixteen. There are two testaments, ten commandments and four gospels.

5. For excellence at Judo.

6. Iron is the metal that comes from the ground after it has been smelted and freed from impurities; steel is iron to which other substances have been added to give it additional properties such as hardness and elasticity. Carbon, for instance, is added to make ordinary steel, and nickel, manganese, tungsten, chrome or vanadium to make steel used for special purposes.

7. They are the symbols for the elements, silver, gold, copper, iron, and nitrogen.

8. A census is a counting of the inhabitants of a country, often nowadays with the collection of additional information about the houses in which they live and so forth. In this country a full census is taken every ten years. The last one was in 1961, so you have probably been concerned in one.

9. In 1952, when the present queen, also called Elizabeth, came to the throne.

10. Hermes, Iris and Mercury.

4

1. A passport. He may also need a visa.

2. The east coast.

3. It is a round disc of leather, rubber, or similar material, and it is used to prevent the water from leaking.

137

4. The beech, but only if it is still young or if it has been kept cut back to form a hedge.

5. Xerxes, Julius Caesar, St Paul, Mohammed, William the Conqueror.

6. Jim Hawkins (in *Treasure Island* by R. L. Stevenson, Chapter 26). Jim and Israel Hands were alone on the 'Hispaniola', and Israel was pursuing Jim to kill him. Jim had just had a chance to change the priming of his pistol which had been made useless by sea-water.

7. The Moors live in Morocco on the north coast of Africa. The Mohawks and the Senecas were two of the Five Nations, the Red Indian tribes living in what is now the State of New York.

8. A bob-sleigh is for two or more people who sit up on it; a toboggan is for one person who usually lies at full length on it head first.

9. Spain has a coastline on both, Portugal on the Atlantic only.

10. Archbishop of Canterbury, and Archbishop of York.

5

1. Merlyn the Magician in *The Sword In The Stone* by T. H. White. (This is the first book of *The Once And Future King*).

2. The centre of the tent was on the north pole.

3. Four Presidents have been assassinated: Abraham Lincoln (1865), J. A. Garfield (1881), William McKinley (1901), and J. F. Kennedy (1963). No English sovereign since 1066 has been assassinated with the possible exception of William II, who was mysteriously shot with an arrow while hunting in

the New Forest. Several kings, e.g. Edward II, Richard II and possibly Edward V, have died in captivity, being put to death by their enemies.

4. A fossil is the remains of a plant or animal of a past age which has, as it were, been turned into stone. A fossil is embedded in ancient rock, and may be found when the lower layers of the earth's surface are exposed on the face of a cliff or in a quarry. Fossils are also sometimes seen in coal.

5. Rice: padi, or paddy, is the Malay word for rice. An Irishman is often called Paddy, from St Patrick, the patron saint of the country.

6. One minute. By the time the guard's van has come out of the tunnel, the engine is already $\frac{1}{2}$ mile away from the exit, so that the engine has travelled one mile since entering the tunnel. 60 m.p.h. is a speed of one mile every minute.

7. Plucking the violin strings with his finger instead of using the bow.

8. Meteorology is the study of the motions and happenings of the atmosphere, especially with a view to forecasting the weather. A meteor is a shooting star. A meteorite is the name given to such a star when it has landed on the earth as a mass of iron and other minerals.

9. 'Breakfast' is the meal that breaks one's fast after one has eaten nothing during the night. Neither the drink nor the word 'tea' was known in Western Europe during the Middle Ages, so there could have been no meal called 'tea'. 'Brunch' is the name sometimes given to a combined breakfast and lunch eaten late in the morning.

10. This was said by Jesus Christ to Peter when they were in the High Priest's house just after Christ's arrest (Matthew,

xxvi, 34). Peter said three times that night during the trial of Jesus Christ that he did not know him.

1. Cowboys – ranch; doves – cote; passengers on a ship – cabins; rabbits – burrow; soldiers – barracks.

2. The city of Venice. (The quotation comes from a poem by Robert Browning – 'A Toccata of Galuppi's'.) The boats are gondolas, or nowadays the *Vaporetti*.

3. It is a dog properly used for hunting the hare, although beagles are often kept as pets.

4. The best known are Van Dyck, the brothers Van Eyck, Van Gogh, Velasquez, Vermeer, Vlaminck, and Vuillard.

5. The look-out on a whaler would exclaim this. A whale has come to the surface and is ejecting water from its blow-holes.

6. General Post Office.

7. Paper that is crimped or pleated. It is specially used for Christmas decorations and artificial flowers. *Crêpe* hair is used by actors to build up false beards, moustaches, etc.

8. Admiral Lord Nelson, after he had been shot on board the *Victory* during the battle of Trafalgar. Captain Hardy was Nelson's flag-captain.

9. Camber is the slight convexity or slope of a road from the middle to the side.

10. There are 100 cents in the dollar, ten in the dime and five in the nickel.

1. An exhibition of cowboy skill in rounding up cattle, riding unbroken horses, etc.

2. The Rhine flows through Germany, Holland and Switzerland; for part of its course it forms the boundary of France, but it does not actually flow through that country.

3. A railway train.

4. He is often called Lawrence of Arabia because of his exploits in that country during the First World War.

5. Arsenal and Tottenham Hotspur; Aston Villa and Birmingham; Everton and Liverpool.

6. Second sight, which some people claim to possess, is the power of seeing events in the future or at a distance as though they were actually present.

7. Badger, field mouse, fox, mole, otter, rabbit, rat, vole, water vole (water rat). The musk rat has been introduced from North America, and the pole cat often 'nests' in a hole dug by another animal.

8. Skimbleshanks is the Railway Cat in a poem by T. S. Eliot. He travelled on the Night Mail train to Scotland.

9. Moccasin, squaw, tepee, wigwam.

10. In stamp collecting.

8

1. Sergeant.

2. You should not overtake when approaching a pedestrian crossing, a road junction, a corner or bend, the brow of a

hill, a hump-back bridge, a place where the road narrows, or where you would have to cross a continuous white line marked on the road, or generally when your overtaking would force another vehicle to swerve or reduce its speed.

3. Properly a hamburger is a round flat cake of finely chopped meat. It is named after the German town of Hamburg and has no connexion with ham.

4. Yes; it has in fact from twenty-nine to forty-two strings.

5. It is part of the eye.

6. Fifteen. There are eight first-round matches, four second-round, two semi-finals, and one final.

7. (i) Out of the frying-pan into the fire. (ii) Six of one and half a dozen of the other. (iii) Least said, soonest mended. (iv) Out of sight, out of mind.

8. The Pope lives in Vatican City, which is strictly a separate city, but is surrounded on all sides by Rome. The U.S.A. President lives in the White House in Washington.

9. It is an agricultural machine that cuts and thrashes the corn in the same operation.

10. She was the goddess of love worshipped by the Romans, and there is a planet of the same name.

9

1. Towards the end of March and September occur the equinoxes, when day and night are of equal length. So by standard time the sun rises at about six in the morning and sets at six in the evening. (By Summer Time it is an hour later.) It rises due east and sets due west.

2. A tanner was a sixpence, a bob was a shilling and a quid a sovereign (20s.).

3. If you multiply 142,857 by 2, 3, 4, 5 or 6, the answer contains the same sequence of numbers, but beginning at a different figure each time.
142,857 × 2 = 285,714   142,857 × 5 = 714,285
142,857 × 3 = 428,571   142,857 × 6 = 857,142
142,857 × 4 = 571,428
The sequence changes when the number is multiplied by 7, and the answer is 999,999.

4. The best known are Raymond, Count of Toulouse, Robert, Duke of Normandy, Godfrey of Bouillon and his brother Baldwin of Jerusalem (all on the first Crusade); the Emperor Frederick I Barbarossa, Philip Augustus of France, and Richard I (Richard Lionheart) of England (on the Third Crusade); and Louis IX of France (Saint Louis) and Prince Edward (later Edward I) of England on the Eighth Crusade.

5. It has very short legs and a very long body. The dachshund is a German dog, bred to hunt badgers in low tunnels underground.

6. Normandy in Europe, Queensland in Australia, Ontario and Texas in North America.

7. Shrove Tuesday is the day before Ash Wednesday, the beginning of Lent, which is six and a half weeks before Easter. Pancakes are traditionally eaten – and tossed – on Shrove Tuesday.

8. Hydrogen was the first gas to be used, but it is very inflammable, and many airships were burnt out. Helium is now frequently used instead, although it is heavier and more expensive, because it is not inflammable.

9. Real pearls come from oysters. A grain of sand or some

143

similar irritant finds its way into the shell, and to cover it up the oyster secretes a substance, which makes the pearl.

10. M1 is a motorway which runs from London to Yorkshire; M.I.5. is the department that deals with counter-espionage.

10

1. St Mark's in Venice; St Paul's in London: St Peter's in Rome (Westminster Abbey is also dedicated to St Peter); Santa Sophia in Istanbul (now a Mohammedan mosque).

2. An airliner built in the U.S.A. A Boeing 747 is the Jumbo Jet which started services in 1970.

3. It is the official survey of Great Britain and Ireland; the results are published in maps of various types which are called Ordnance Survey maps.

4. Dr Samuel Johnson.

5. They are *couturiers*, the heads of fashion houses.

6. The blackbird (the male only); the thrush.

7. Harvard and Yale.

8. No. His body would seem to be three times as heavy as on Mars since the pull of gravity here is three times what it is on Mars.

9. E.R. stands for Elizabeth Regina – Queen Elizabeth. You are most likely to see the letters on something connected with the Post Office – a pillar or post box, or a mail van, or perhaps on an official letter.

10. Crab apples; hot ale.

1. A 'dig' usually means an archaeological excavation site; 'digs' (short for 'diggings') is a slang term for lodgings; and a 'digger', apart from its obvious meaning of 'one who digs', is an Australian, or less commonly a New Zealander.

2.   (i) A peck of March dust is worth a king's ransom.
  (ii) When the wind is in the east,
     It's good for neither man nor beast.

3. A motel is an hotel for motorists. It comes from mo(tor) and (ho)tel. It is on or very near a main road and is properly made up of units, each one providing accommodation for a car and its passengers.

4. You see pebble-dash on the outside walls of houses; it is mortar on which small pebbles have been dashed so that they stick.

5. It is the Irish for 'Ireland for ever!'

6. The battles of Hastings (1066), in which Harold I died; and of Bosworth (1485), in which Richard III died.

7. Everest (29,141 ft), Kilimanjaro (19,321 ft), Mont Blanc (15,782 ft), Ben Nevis (4,406 ft), Snowdon (3,560 ft).

8. King Arthur's wife was Queen Guinevere, and Robin Hood's wife was Maid Marian.

9. Lighting-up time begins half an hour after sunset, and ends half an hour before sunrise.

10. His name was Pontius Pilate. He asked 'Art thou the King of the Jews?' and 'What is truth?'

1. First-aid is help given before the arrival of a doctor to someone who has been injured. The St John Ambulance Brigade trains its members to provide first-aid.

2. The Antarctic regions are opposite to the Arctic regions. If you dug down from England you would come to a spot in the South Pacific to the south-west of New Zealand.

3. The door to the cave full of robbers' treasure in the story *Ali Baba and the Forty Thieves*.

4. Robinson Crusoe, in the story by Daniel Defoe. Man Friday was rescued by Crusoe from cannibals who had brought him to Crusoe's island intending to kill and eat him.

5. If by dark we mean total darkness, as in a building with all its windows sealed, the answer is 'no'. In the open at night there is, however, always a certain amount of light present, and the eyes of these creatures are specially adapted to have good vision under minimum light conditions.

6. On the number-plate of a car fairly recently registered.

7. Alexander the Great; Alfred the Great of England; Catherine the Great of Russia; Charles the Great, often called Charlemagne, of France; Frederick the Great of Prussia; Herod the Great; Peter the Great of Russia.

8. Israel and Jordan.

9. Roasting and grinding.

10. There is no such place. It is a name formed from *Ox*ford and Cam*bridge* to distinguish these, the two ancient universities of England, from those which have come into existence in the nineteenth and twentieth centuries.

1. Wembley Stadium.

2. (i) 0, − 4, − 8
   (ii) 1, $\frac{1}{3}$, $\frac{1}{9}$
   (iii) 22, 28, 35

3. De Gaulle – France; Eisenhower and MacArthur – U.S.A.;
   Montgomery and Wavell – Britain; Rommel – Germany.

4. A Roman god.

5. Members of the Royal Canadian Mounted Police Force.

6. Oxford, Reading, Henley, Maidenhead, London.

7. In Britain we grow wheat, oats, barley, and rye; in the
   U.S.A. maize or Indian corn also.

8. Highlands.

9. (a) One pint. (b) $\frac{1}{3}$ pint.

10. Very little. It has no value as a fertilizer, though it may be
    used to lighten heavy soils, to cover bulbs in bowls intended
    to grow indoors, and to prevent slugs from harming the
    crowns of plants.

1. Giovanni – Italy; Ian – Scotland; Ivan – Russia; Jean –
   France; Johann – Germany; Juan – Spain; Sean – Ireland.

2. A stretch of road along which the stopping of cars for any
   reason except a breakdown is prohibited.

3. With Allan Quatermain, and the expedition was to discover King Solomon's Mines (in the story of that name by Rider Haggard.)

4. At the bottom of the wall of a room in a house.

5. The battle of Waterloo (18 June 1815) in which he finally defeated Napoleon I.

6. *Hors d'œuvres*, soup, fish, entrée, roast, sweet, cheese, coffee.

7. Penelope, the wife of Ulysses. Her husband was away for twenty years fighting at and returning from Troy, and many suitors, believing he was dead, wanted to marry her. Penelope promised that she would choose one of them when she had finished the tapestry, but unpicked it every night to delay finishing it.

8. Cockles, mussels, oysters, scallops, whelks and winkles are shell-fish. There are also crabs, lobsters, prawns and shrimps, which are properly called crustaceans.

9. It was originally carried for sharpening quill pens.

10. (a) At the Straits of Gibraltar, at the western end of the Mediterranean Sea. (b) Asia and North America.

15

1. St Valentine's Day.

2. The names are Byzantium and Constantinople. (There is also the form Stamboul sometimes found for Istanbul.) The city is situated on the Bosporus, the strait that leads from the Sea of Marmora to the Black Sea.

3. Tinder was dry inflammable material used before the invention of matches to take fire from a spark struck from flint and steel. The tinder-box contained the tinder and usually the flint and steel.

4. It is behind Table Bay in the extreme south of Africa, at Cape Town.

5. They are trade number plates and are used by garages so that cars which are not licensed or insured can be taken on the road for tests, demonstrations, or delivery.

6. The Pied Piper in Robert Browning's poem, 'The Pied Piper of Hamelin'. He undertook to free Hamelin of its plague of rats for a thousand guilders.

7. Circe was a sorceress who lived in the island of Aeaea and was visited by Ulysses. She had the power of changing human beings into animals, and all the companions of Ulysses became swine. Ulysses himself was not changed because of the magical power of a herb named moly.

8. Horses eat grass, hay, oats and barley, peas and beans, and bran (but wheat is not suitable for them). Delicacies are apples and sugar.

9. The line of life is on your hand; in palmistry it is the crease in the left hand running from above the thumb towards the wrist. The nearer it approaches the wrist, the longer will be the life, according to the palmists.

10. Esperanto is spoken in almost every country in the world, though by only a few people. It is an international language made up from very simple words and roots, which its inventors hoped would become universally used.

1. The engine driver and fireman.

2. Headingley, Moss Side and Solihull.

3. It bores into wood, especially the beams of old houses. It makes a clicking noise, which was supposed to foretell a death in the house.

4. In a story by Mary Wollstonecraft Shelley (published in 1818) Frankenstein made a monster in the shape of a human being and gave it life. The monster hated the man who had created it and finally killed him. Frankenstein is often wrongly used as the name of the monster. (The story has been turned into a film.)

5. A building society builds nothing itself, but it lends money to people who wish to build (or more usually buy) houses.

6. Michelangelo, Raphael, Titian.

7. Brisket is a joint of meat.

8. John Churchill, Duke of Marlborough (1650–1722), the victor of Blenheim.

9. Celtic and Rangers.

10. Aluminium is very light and does not corrode. Aluminium is the English and aluminum the American spelling of the word; there is no other difference.

1. Yes, the tank.

2. The compass always points towards the magnetic pole, but the position of this varies considerably; so the compass changes its direction from century to century.

3. It is to warn drivers that the vehicle has a very wide load or is otherwise likely to obstruct the flow of traffic.

4. In the song John Brown's body lies a-mouldering in the grave, but his soul goes marching on.

5. He was born in Corsica and died on St Helena. His full name was Napoléon Buonaparte (or Bonaparte as it is usually spelled in English).

6. Something to do with postage stamps.

7. A meeting of Welsh bards and musicians which is held in Wales. The word is correctly spelled in the question.

8. The mountain was in northern Greece, and the gods of the Greeks were supposed to live there ruled over by Zeus, their king.

9. (a) 9 dozen are 108; 5 score are 100.
   (b) Both are 3.
   (c) 479 halfpence; 239 pence are only 478 halfpence.
   (d) ½ of 5 × 12 is 30; the other answer is 29.
   (e) Three to the fourth is 81; two to the fifth is only 32.
   (f) There are 84 inches, but only 83 pence.

10. The heart and the lungs.

1. A fender might be before a hearth, between the side of a ship and the quay, or on a car. A fender is something that fends or wards off something else, and all fenders are used to prevent damage to what they protect.

2. Other solutions are like this arrangement turned on its side, upside-down or back to front.

8	1	6
3	5	7
4	9	2

3. A Very Important Person.

4. The lobster (*Alice's Adventures In Wonderland*, Chapter 10). The Walrus and the Carpenter (*Through the Looking-Glass*, Chapter 4).

5. Montmartre is part of Paris. St Michael's Mount is a promontory in the far west of Cornwall. There is also Mont St Michel, a rocky islet off the coast of north-west France.

6. Five trains. Suppose the passenger caught the 10 a.m. train. As it was leaving, the 8 a.m. train from Whybury arrived. When his train got to Whybury, the 12 o'clock train from Whybury was just leaving, and he would have seen the 9, 10 and 11 o'clock trains on the way.

7. When Achilles was a baby his mother, Thetis, dipped him in the River Styx to make him invulnerable; but she held him by the heel and the water did not reach this part. It was from a wound in the heel that he died. The phrase nowadays is used to refer to the weak point of a man.

8. The Siamese cat.

9. John Constable.

10. In Egypt.

19

1. He finds it difficult to go to sleep.

2. A mitre is a tall pointed head-dress worn by a bishop or other dignitary of the Catholic church. A mitre is also a joint in woodwork made by a carpenter.

3. Lindisfarne is an island off the coast of Northumberland; it is sometimes called Holy Island because of the ruined monastery on it.

4. Dick Whittington, while he was going away from London because of the ill-treatment he had received there, rested at Holloway and imagined he heard Bow Bells ringing and telling him.

> 'Turn again, Whittington,
> Thrice Lord Mayor of London'.

5. It is the international radio-telephonic distress signal for ships and aircraft. It comes from the French '*m'aidez*', help me.

6. (a) 41 (or 25 in our own number system).
   (b) 15 (or 11 in our own number system).
   (c) 123 (or 51 in our own number system).

7. They are the chemical symbols for water – denoting two atoms of hydrogen and one of oxygen.

8. There is a four-leaved clover (or rather a leaf made up of four and not the usual three leaflets), but it is rare and to find one is supposed to bring good luck. A clover-leaf is also the name applied to a junction in which one road passes over the top of another, and the roads connecting the two are in the pattern of a four-leaved clover so that the turns are not abrupt or against the traffic.

9. On the east coast of Northern Ireland.

10. Julius Caesar spoke in Latin, St Paul wrote in Greek.

20

1. A patten is a kind of wooden overshoe mounted on an iron ring and fastened under the shoe to raise the feet above the mud.

2. The car is braking.

3. No.

4. Cine-film.

5. 'Pianoforte' means 'soft-loud'. (The original Italian was 'piano e forte').

6. Gendarmes are found in France. They are members of a military force used to preserve public order and performing many of the functions of the police.

7. Cardiff.

8. Haroun-al-Raschid figures in many of the stories of *The Arabian Nights Entertainment*. Though the stories have no basis in fact, Haroun was actually the Caliph of Baghdad at the end of the eighth century.

9. Hitch-hiking is travelling by obtaining lifts on vehicles. Thumbing a lift is indicating by the motion of your thumb to the driver of a lorry or car that you would like a lift along the road.

10. First he weighs two sets of three coins. If they balance, the odd coin is in the other set of three. If they do not balance, the odd coin is in the lighter set of three.

Secondly he takes two of the three coins left as possibles, and weighs them against each other. If they balance, the other coin is light. If they do not balance, he has found the lighter one.

21

1. He rules over Greece.

2. The Jumblies (in Edward Lear's poem) went to sea in a sieve, the butcher, the baker, and the candlestick-maker sailed in a tub, and the wise men of Gotham in a bowl.

3. Each of the four wheels of the car is sprung separately so that they operate independently when the car is going over bumps.

4. A marmoset is a small American monkey; a marmot is a burrowing rodent called in America the woodchuck. The tongue-twister begins: 'How much wood would a woodchuck chuck if a woodchuck could chuck wood?'

5. $\dfrac{31}{32}$

6. A licence is needed for a dog (except in special cases), but not for a cat or a horse.

7. The first jockey was Gordon Richards, the first cricketer J. B. Hobbs, and the first footballer Stanley Matthews.

8. As Santa Claus.

9. A chopper is a helicopter; another name for it is 'whirly-bird'.

10. A criminal. The gallows where public executions took place were at Tyburn, close to where Marble Arch now stands.

22

1. He was born in Stratford-on-Avon.

2. Yes, if it causes annoyance to the residents or the passers-by.

3. Troy was also called Ilium. It was situated on the extreme north-west of Asia Minor, where the Dardanelles joins the Aegean Sea.

4. A slalom is a ski race in which technical skill is required, especially a zigzag run between posts or flags.

5. At Paddington.

6. On an aerodrome. It is material shaped like a large funnel to indicate to pilots the direction of the wind.

7. From wheat.

8. In the parable told by Jesus Christ the Good Samaritan

helped a man who had been attacked and was left lying at the roadside by people who passed by. The injured man was a Jew and the people who would not help him were also Jews. The Samaritans were another race who disliked the Jews and were disliked by them, and yet it was a Samaritan who helped the Jew. Jesus wished to teach that all men are neighbours of one another.

9. The birth must be registered.

10. May is not an autumn month in the northern hemisphere; the poem is about a country south of the equator (in actual fact Australia). May there corresponds to our November.

23

1. An acid.

2. It is a musical instrument.

3. Alpha and beta, from which comes the word alphabet.

4. They were called 'The Three Musketeers' (in the novel by Alexandre Dumas). Their companion was d'Artagnan.

5. A railway in the U.S.A.

6. Sand consists of tiny particles of rock which has been worn away by water or possibly wind.

7. A reporter makes a scoop when he obtains and publishes an important piece of news earlier than anyone else.

8. He would live in Yorkshire, in the part which contains such towns as Leeds, Bradford and Sheffield.

9. To Moses, on the top of Mount Sinai.

10. Norman, Plantagenet, Lancastrian, Tudor, Stuart, Windsor (to which our present sovereign belongs.)

24

1. Paris and Lisbon.

2. Clap them together in time to music; they are two pieces of ivory or hard wood.

3. Jupiter. It has twelve moons.

4. God worked for six days, and 'he rested on the seventh day from all his work which God created and made'.

5. Butter is made from cream, and cheese from whole or sometimes skimmed milk. The cream is churned or agitated until it becomes butter; the milk is curdled and the whey or remaining liquid run off, and then the substance is pressed until it is hard and dry and becomes cheese.

6. Cuttlefish, squids and octopuses use jet propulsion, which moves them through the water very rapidly. They take in water through their mouth and then thrust the water out through a sort of funnel. Some shell fish also use a form of jet propulsion.

7. The Lady of Shalott (in the poem by Lord Tennyson).

8. It is a warning; a vehicle with air brakes can stop more quickly than one with ordinary brakes.

9. Snowdrop and tulip.

10. He knew that sound travelled at approximately $\frac{1}{5}$ mile a second. He timed the gap between the firing of the gun and the echo of the shot, which was four seconds. The sound

must have taken two seconds to reach the cliff and two seconds to echo back, so he knew that the cliff was approximately $\frac{2}{5}$ of a mile, or 700 yards, away.

25

1. The East Indies, in particular the Moluccas, from which spices were imported to Europe.

2. Charles II, who had left England in 1651 after his defeat in the battle of Worcester in the Civil War.

3. Wood; a joiner is much the same as a carpenter.

4. A truncheon.

5. Interpol is the *Inter*national *Pol*ice Commission for co-operation against criminals.

6. Oliver Goldsmith.

7. He let the air out of the front tyres so that the van was freed, backed it away on the flat tyres and blew the tyres up again. By this method he had to avoid the bridge by finding another route, but he could also have let all the tyres down and tried to drive the van under the bridge in that state.

8.

> 'Jack and Jill went up the hill
> To fetch a pail of water.'

The Ancient Mariner (in the poem by S. T. Coleridge) saw water all around, but it was salt sea water and unfit for drinking.

9. Apollo and Diana.

10. At an auction there is no stated price; an article is put up for sale, offers or bids are indicated and the highest bidder obtains the article.

26

1. A shambles is properly a butcher's stall or a slaughter-house, and The Shambles was the street of the butchers. The word came to be used of any place of slaughter such as a battlefield, and now it often means simply a place of complete disorder.

2. Leather is made by tanning the skins of animals.

3. A burning-glass is a convex lens for concentrating the rays of the sun so that great heat is produced; paper, etc., can be set on fire in this way.

4. Usually one. During the summer one or more new queens may be reared, but only one remains in the hive; the others leave with 'swarms' to start new colonies.

5. In summer the shadow would lie to the south-west, and in winter to the north-west.

6. They were originally groups of mounted Boers in the South African War. In the Second World War they were special troops trained for dangerous assault tasks.

7. Fried potatoes.

8. The Humber.

9. *Swallows and Amazons* by Arthur Ransome.

10. One of the main ways of cooling off when we are hot is to perspire. If the atmosphere is hot and humid (damp) the

sweat does not evaporate, and we have difficulty in cooling. If it is dry and hot the perspiration evaporates quickly and we are kept reasonably cool. It is for the same reason that clothes hanging out to dry on a hot humid day will dry much more slowly than on a dry warm one.

27

1. Gnomes were supposed to live underground, where they were the guardians of the treasures of the earth in mines and quarries.

2. They were Roman centurions who fought on the Great Wall against the Winged Hats from across the North Sea. We read about them in two stories by Rudyard Kipling, 'On the Great Wall' and 'The Winged Hats', both of them in *Puck of Pook's Hill*.

3. D-Day is 6 June 1944, the day when the Allied troops landed in Normandy to reconquer Europe from the Germans.

4. Ichthyosaurus, iguanodon, mastodon, pterodactyl.

5. 'A biue' is a man who has been chosen to represent his university – Oxford or Cambridge – at a sport. Oxford awards a 'dark blue', and Cambridge a 'light blue'. The Blues are the Royal Horse Guards, and also melancholy Negro songs. (The blues are the dumps.)

6. David killed Goliath in this way (1 Samuel, Chapter xvii).

7. Chiefly from the sugar-cane and the sugar-beet, and some from the maple.

8. With Nottingham Forest Football Club, and Nottingham-shire County Cricket Club.

9. Treble or soprano.

10. Coventry and Detroit.

28

1. To go 'on safari' is to go on a hunting expedition, especially in the interior of Africa.

2. Anglesey is joined to Wales.

3. Triffids are described in a novel by John Wyndham, *The Day Of The Triffids*. They are grotesque plants, over seven feet tall, which become a menace to humanity and kill almost every human being.

4. Chaps are cracks, especially those caused in the skin by cold (we speak of 'chapped hands'); chaps are fellows or men, and they are the jaws of an animal; the word is a short form of '*chaparejos*', the leather riding leggings of a cowboy.

5. With rare exceptions fish lay eggs, often called roe or spawn.

6. Wednesday is the day of Woden, the Anglo-Saxon king of the gods. March is the month of Mars, the Roman god of war. Julius Caesar was born in the month that was later named July after him.

7. A light dish, either sweet or savoury, made by mixing the materials with white of egg beaten up to a froth, and heating the mixture in the oven until it puffs up.

8. A cat may look at a king.

9. A vegetarian is a person who lives upon vegetable foods, and refuses to eat food that has been obtained by killing an

animal. There are some vegetarians who go so far as to abstain from all foods obtained from animals, including milk and eggs.

10. 'Buzzing' occurs when one plane interferes with another in the air by flying very near to it.

29

1. C is 100, D is 500, and M is 1000. 3, 5, and 9 are Arabic numerals.

2. No, they were not grown here until the eighteenth century.

3. The ship was coming from the Isthmus of Panama, and was carrying

> 'Diamonds,
> Emeralds, amethysts,
> Topazes, and cinnamon, and gold moidores.'

4. It is the French for born, and is used before the woman's maiden name.

5. It is used in the making of transistors, and radio sets and other electronic apparatus are much smaller than they were when valves were used.

6. Pasta is the Italian word used for specialities made from flour – macaroni, spaghetti, vermicelli, noodles.

7. Dunkirk was the scene of the successful evacuation by sea of the British army at the beginning of June 1940, when the Germans were over-running Northern France.

8. A metronome is an instrument with an inverted pendulum that can be set to beat so many times a minute, and thus regulate the speed of performance of a piece of music.

9. Because of the 24-hour motor race held on this circuit.

10. The sirens were sea-nymphs, part woman and part bird, who lured sailors to destruction by their sweet singing. Nowadays a siren is an apparatus that signals or warns by a high loud note; sirens were used during the Second World War to give notice of the approach and departure of enemy aircraft.

30

1. People went to Delphi to consult the oracle there by asking the priestess of Apollo to obtain answers from the god to their questions.

2. An old Portuguese gold coin.

3. Shanghai is in China, and Tokyo in Japan.

4. Duffle coat; dirndl skirt; stetson hat.

5. Only the hedgehog, and to some extent the squirrel.

6. Glasses with two segments of different focal lengths, the top part for distant vision and the lower for reading.

7. He was Charles Edward, the grandson of James II; he is sometimes called the Young Pretender, and he led the 1745 rebellion in an attempt to gain the throne of Great Britain.

8. Since the cheque was destroyed it could not be presented at a bank and the £100 could not be paid to anybody; so all that the man lost was twopence, the cost of the stamp on the cheque.

9. Michelangelo (1475–1564).

10. In the Northern Hemisphere the Pole Star is always visible to sailors near the north pole of the heavens and they used it to steer by. The stars called the Pointers in the Great Bear (Ursa Major) show the line to the Pole Star.

31

1. The Dodo in *Alice's Adventures in Wonderland* organized a caucus race in which everybody had a prize.

2. On the east are Yorkshire, Durham and Northumberland; on the west Lancashire, Westmorland and Cumberland.

3. Deniers are used to measure the thickness of nylon thread especially for stockings, and watts to measure electric power.

4. A supersonic aircraft flies faster than the speed of sound. It makes a supersonic bang when it crosses the sound barrier – that is, when it begins to fly faster than sound.

5. The man had played the ball a second time without its having been touched by another player, and this is not allowed after a penalty.

6. A whip is an M.P. who sees that members of his party are in attendance at the House of Commons. It is also short for 'whipper-in', the man who manages the fox-hounds in the hunting field.

7. A bantam is a very small variety of hen. The name is also used of any very small person, especially a soldier; there were Bantam battalions formed during the First World War.

8. A ballet with music by Tchaikovsky.

9. Most Negroes live in the south-eastern States, though some of them are moving to the north. Their ancestors were

brought from Africa to work as slaves, in particular in the cotton plantations.

10. The Somme in the First World War, and El Alamein in the Second.

32

1. A dodo was a bird, rather larger than a swan; it used to live in Mauritius, but it is now extinct. The phrase is 'as dead as the dodo'.

2. An anemometer is an instrument for measuring the speed of wind. Force 11 indicates a wind speed of approximately 70 m.p.h. Such a wind would cause much damage to trees and the roofs of buildings, etc.

3. A clam is a shell-fish very popular in America; to be like a clam is to be silent, to shut oneself up and give no information.

4. 'No Man's Land' was the strip of territory that ran between the enemy trenches in France and Flanders during the First World War.

5. The Romans conquered southern Scotland but did not hold it long. They never tried to conquer Ireland.

6. On the Ganges – Calcutta (also Benares, Allahabad and Lucknow); on the Nile – Alexandria, Cairo and Khartoum.

7. Sherlock Holmes to Dr Watson (in Sir Arthur Conan Doyle's story The 'Gloria Scott').

8. (a) Silver; (b) Nickel.

9. The Philistines lived on the eastern coast of the Mediterranean Sea. They were the enemies of the Jews.

10. The referee, though he should take into account anything the linesman has to say.

33

1. The person most often put forward is Francis Bacon, but many other men have been suggested.

2. U.S.S.R. (the Union of Soviet Socialist Republics, or Russia) and China.

3. They are made of earthenware, that is, baked clay.

4. Grace was born in 1848 and died in 1915, so that he lived in both centuries, but his great days were in the nineteenth century.

5. Old, new, borrowed, blue.

6. Elvers are young eels.

7. 'O God, our help in ages past.'

8. (a) The Celts; (b) the Anglo-Saxons; (c) the Anglo-Saxons.

9. One ring to stop; two rings to start; and three in an emergency.

10. They are both interested in food; a gourmet is a person with a delicate taste in food and wine, a gourmand is a gluttonous and greedy eater.

34

1. That the car is about to turn in the direction indicated.

2. Thomas à Becket in Canterbury Cathedral (1170).

3. Kilns are used for burning, baking and drying. Lime is burnt in them, bricks and pottery baked, and hops dried.

4. The forget-me-not.

5. The sum of ten odd numbers is never odd.

6. They were both pioneers of printing. Gutenberg, who died in 1468, was one of the earliest of German printers, and Caxton, who had previously printed abroad several books in English, set up the first press in this country in 1477.

7. It was in a covered wagon that the American pioneers went westward over the prairies.

8. Ixion was bound on a burning wheel that turned for ever, and Sisyphus had to roll to the top of a hill a huge stone which always rolled down again when it had almost reached the top. Tantalus was punished with intense hunger and thirst; though he was up to the chin in water and a bough laden with food was just above his head, the drink and the food moved away when he tried to reach them. (From this story we get the word 'tantalize').

9. Spots from one to six in number.

10. The metre is longer, being about 39·37 inches. The kilogram is heavier, about 2·205 pounds.

35

1. Bath, known to the Romans as Aquae Sulis.

2. The reserve for a cricket or football team.

3. (a) Chow; (b) saluki; (c) poodle.

4. Aswan is on the river Nile in Egypt. It is well known for its dams which store up water for irrigation.

5. Centrifugal force makes a body revolving about a centre tend to fly off from its curved path, and centripetal force makes it tend to move towards the attracting point at the centre.

6. The father killed the fatted calf for the prodigal son in the parable told by Jesus (Luke xv, 11–32).

7. A railway station in London, a state of Australia and a city on Vancouver Island are named Victoria; there are Lake Victoria and the Victoria Falls in Central Africa; there are the Victoria Cross, the Victoria plum and the Victoria sandwich (a sort of cake). There is the Victoria Embankment in London, and perhaps we can include the Victoria and Albert Museum. There was also a carriage called a victoria.

8. P. G. Wodehouse has written many novels and short stories about Jeeves, the man-servant of Bertie Wooster.

9. $7\frac{1}{4}$ lb.

10. A dormer window projects from a sloping roof; it is a small window with a gable.

36

1. At Jodrell Bank there is a radio telescope, and at Goonhilly Down a space communications station which receives messages bounced off satellites.

2. A doctor uses a stethoscope for detecting sounds in the heart and the lungs.

3. The gods of the Greeks were supposed to drink nectar; their food was called ambrosia.

4. The arrow is an indication that a driver must keep well in to his own side because of a curve or something similar just ahead.

5. 5 November celebrates the unsuccessful attempt in 1605 by Guy Fawkes and his fellow conspirators to blow up the Houses of Parliament.

6. Not quite; it is a few miles inland up the river Tiber.

7. Elephant Bill; he is the author of a book of that name, which describes his experiences with elephants.

8. The birth of Jesus Christ.

9. An over has six or eight balls. In the United Kingdom there are six unless an agreement to the contrary has been made, but in Australia there are eight.

10. Linseed oil is the recognized medium, but many modern painters use turpentine, which is properly a spirit.

37

1. An argonaut was a voyager in the ship Argo – one of those who went with Jason in quest of the Golden Fleece (nautes is the Greek word for sailor). The other words have been formed recently to mean space-explorers – literally, 'sailor towards the stars' and 'sailor in the cosmos' or universe.

2. The cauliflower, broccoli and the flower of the globe artichoke.

3. The question is 'When did England go to war with Hitler's Germany?'

4. Cornwall.

5. During a boat race, since the oarsmen face the stern of the boat and so are looking backwards.

6. Pylons.

7. Curry was originally made in India; another meaning of the word is 'to rub down and dress a horse with a comb'.

8. (a) Mercy; (b) music; (c) throne, scepter'd, majesty, Mars; (d) thyme; (e) pensioners.

9. It was used to prove that the earth is rotating. When the pendulum swung freely it always deviated on its return to the right showing that the ground supporting the column was moving and therefore the earth was rotating. Such a pendulum can be seen in the Science Museum in London.

10. A dog in the manger is a person who has something he himself has no use for and yet will not allow anybody else to have. A fable tells how a dog lying in a manger would not let the cattle come near to eat the hay he could not himself eat.

38

1. Joan of Arc (1412–31) who led the French army against the English in the Hundred Years' War.

2. Tides are caused chiefly by the gravitational influence of the moon, and to a lesser extent the sun on the water in the sea. The strength of this force varies at different times of the month. Spring tides are just after a new or full moon when the attraction is strongest so that the tides are highest; neap tides are just after the first or third quarter of the moon when the reverse is true. There are practically no tides in land-locked seas like the Mediterranean.

3. Trafalgar Square.

4. The Charred Cross is in Coventry Cathedral; it is made from beams charred in the German air raid of 1940 and stands in the ruined sanctuary of the old cathedral.

5. Exploring the caves and passages worn by water in limestone rocks.

6. A frieze is a decorated band along the top of the wall of a room, or a rough woollen cloth; a freesia is a flowering plant; and a Friesian is a breed of cattle.

7. Hamlet's father was also named Hamlet. The younger Hamlet was commanded to kill his uncle Claudius, who had murdered the elder Hamlet.

8. The letter E.

9. The dinosaur is an extinct reptile that lived many millions of years ago. You may, however, see its fossil skeleton in a museum or even a life-size model of it.

10. (a) Tudor.
    (b) Georgian.

39

1. Cumulus is the best type of cloud for gliding. It is a heaped up cloud caused by rising currents of air – a smaller edition of the thunder cloud. The rising air currents enable the glider to keep aloft.

2. The ox, though horses were becoming more common towards the end of the Middle Ages.

3. Rupert was the villain; he worked against the Princess Flavia and Rudolf Rassendyl.

4. Ballet; opera ('musical' would do except for 'an'); film or TV play; animated cartoon; mime.

5. Oil, and bottled gas.

6. A frogman is an underwater swimmer in a rubber suit with paddles on his feet resembling frog's legs; the term was used especially during the Second World War of men who entered enemy harbours at night and attached explosives to blow up ships. The frog's march is a method of carrying a refractory person face downwards between four men, each holding one limb.

7. An aspidistra is a plant with large leaves, once very popular for the house.

8. Anti-Semitism is hatred and persecution of the Jews. It was very common in Hitler's Germany during the 1930s and the Second World War.

9. Calvary, or Golgotha, a hill just outside Jerusalem.

10. Rubber; it makes in particular tyres for cars.

40

1. It is an animal, a baboon.

2. Z-cars are police patrol cars equipped with two-way radio; there has been a popular B.B.C. television series about them.

3. A fountain pen, or a camera.

4. They tend to move upwards.

5. A driver, an iron and a putter.

6. Prospero of Caliban (in Shakespeare's play *The Tempest*, I, ii). Trinculo was the other speaker (*The Tempest*, II, ii).

7. Stonehenge is on Salisbury Plain in Wiltshire. It was apparently erected over a long period, but the main structure is probably the work of the Bronze Age, perhaps about 1500 B.C. The great stones came from the Preseli Hills in Pembrokeshire.

8. It is a painting by Frans Hals.

9. The dog was trained to track and help travellers lost in the snow in the St Bernard passes over the Alps. On the Great St Bernard there is the hospice founded by and named after St Bernard of Menthon.

10. He needed a 3 lb. weight.

Weight measured in lb.	Weights pan	Goods pan
1	1	
2	3	1
3	3	
4	3 + 1	
5	9	3 + 1
6	9	3

and so on . . .

41

1. A cattle-grid is a grating across a roadway, so that cars can pass across but cattle cannot. It is found in the country instead of a gate across the road.

2. (a) Alfred Jingle in *The Pickwick Papers*; (b) Sidney Carton in *A Tale Of Two Cities*.

3. Shannon.

4. Gloucestershire – Hammond; Nottinghamshire – Larwood; Sussex – Tate; Yorkshire – Rhodes and Sutcliffe.

5. Blind people. The letters are represented by groups of embossed dots which can be read by the fingers.

6. The White Ensign is flown by ships of the Royal Navy, and the Red by ships of the Merchant Navy.

7. Beaumaris (in Anglesey), Caernarvon, Conway, Harlech are the best-known.

8. In a blood bank is kept refrigerated blood which has been given by blood donors for transfusion to people in hospital who have lost much blood from an accident or operation.

9. The prophecy was that whoever untied the Gordian knot would reign over the whole East, but Alexander the Great simply cut through it with his sword.

10. If you were swimming in the sea you would probably come ashore; the Portuguese man-of-war is a kind of jelly-fish with a sharp sting.

42

1. The Old Bailey is a street in London in which stands the Central Criminal Court; trials for murders and other serious crimes committed in London are held here. It is on the site of Newgate Prison, very close to Holborn Viaduct.

2. The skunk is a small American mammal of the marten family; when attacked it gives off an evil-smelling liquid. A mean contemptible fellow is sometimes called a skunk.

3. During a race a car goes to the pits for repairs and re-fuelling.

4. A 35-mm. camera.

5. One was the first *king* of the *Israelites*; the other changed his name to *Paul* and is thought to have died a martyr's death in *Rome*.

6. Fox-hunting is from 1 November to the end of March usually; cub-hunting begins at the end of August and continues to the end of October.

7. The jolly swagman in the Australian song 'Waltzing Matilda', by Andrew ('Banjo') Paterson. A 'matilda' was a tramp's roll or bag, and 'waltzing Matilda' was tramping.

8. In North America; it is one of the United States.

9. A berserk was originally a Norse warrior who became seized with uncontrollable fury on the battle-field. Nowadays a person who completely loses control of himself and becomes violent is said 'to go berserk'.

10. Mineral, properly a form of magnesium silicate.

43

1. A locum tenens is a person who takes over temporarily the duties of someone else. Doctors and clergymen, when they go on holiday, often employ a locum tenens to attend to their patients or to take their services.

2. Hiawatha was the hero of the American Indians. The poem 'Hiawatha' was written by the American Henry Wadsworth Longfellow, who says that Hiawatha belonged to the Ojibway tribe.

3. Telepathy may be called 'thought-transference'; it is the power that some people claim to possess of communicating thoughts without the use of speech, and perhaps over long distances.

4. Daniel was thrown into a den of lions (Daniel, vi) because being a Jew, he refused to worship King Darius. It is usually said that Jonah was swallowed by a whale, though in the Bible (Jonah, i, 17) we read simply that 'the Lord had prepared a great fish to swallow up Jonah'.

5. Highwaymen, when they were holding up travellers.

6. To a sailor the fairway is the navigable channel in a river; to a golfer it is the smooth turf between the tee and the green, as distinguished from the uncut grass on either side known as the rough.

7. Norway, Denmark and Sweden.

8. It is several ounces under half a pound.

9. The Stone of Destiny forms part of the Coronation Throne in Westminster Abbey. Until 1297 it was at Scone in Scotland and on it the kings of Scotland were crowned, but in that year Edward I believed that he had conquered Scotland and brought the stone to England as a sign of this.

10. In New Orleans.

44

1. Through hardships to the stars.

2. It is a disease of parrots and similar birds.

3. You probably know the book *Born Free* by Joy Adamson

about Elsa the lioness; but the phrase was originally used by St Paul about himself, meaning that he was a free-born Roman citizen.

4. Easter Island is famous for its huge idols which are made out of single blocks of stone and some of which reach twenty feet in height. Little is known about when or by whom they were made.

5. You go west to reach San Francisco from Chicago, though you could reach it by travelling east round the world. You go south from Montreal to New York.

6. To 50 million. In the last census in 1961 it was 52,676,000.

7. Either brother-in-law or sister-in-law.

8. Queen Elizabeth I ordered the execution of Mary, Queen of Scots (1587).

9.   (a) *Round the World in Eighty Days* (Jules Verne).
    (b) *Three Men in a Boat* (Jerome K. Jerome).
    (c) *The Sign of Four* (A. Conan Doyle).

10. To avoid the best players being drawn against each other in the early rounds, in many tournaments some of them, usually eight, are selected and each is placed in a different part of the draw. This is called 'seeding'.

45

1. Plankton is the name given to the various forms, usually very small, of organic life that drift about in water, especially the sea.

2. The Pyramids are in Egypt. They were constructed as tombs for some of the Pharaohs. The largest are the Pyramids of Gizeh, which are over 4,500 years old.

3. Chevrolet – U.S.A.; Fiat – Italy; Jaguar – England; Renault – France; Volkswagen – Germany; Volvo – Sweden; Zim – U.S.S.R.

4. The Backs are in Cambridge – the bank of the river Cam, to which the gardens of several of the Colleges come down. The Broads are in Norfolk – a series of fresh-water lakes joined together by streams.

5. The Globe was a theatre on the south side of the river Thames in Southwark. It was the scene of the first production of many of Shakespeare's plays.

6. They have roughly the same shape, but the blade of a shovel is broad and more or less hollow with upturned sides. A spade is used for digging, and a shovel for lifting and moving loose material.

7. Australia, South Africa, New Zealand, West Indies, India, Pakistan.

8. In the eighteenth century, in the War of Independence, 1775–84.

9. The Valkyries were the Choosers of the Slain, the women who, the Norsemen believed, chose the heroes who were to die in battle, and conducted them to Valhalla, the Norse heaven.

10. Diesel oil comes from petroleum.

46

1. The U.S.A. and Mexico.

2. A fell is the skin or hide of an animal, a northern term for an upland tract of moorland or a mountain, and a name for a hemming stitch.

3. The buttercup (in the poem 'Home-Thoughts, from Abroad').

4. The presence of lamp standards for street lighting.

5. A Scotch egg is a hard-boiled egg surrounded by a layer of sausage-meat and then fried. A duck's egg is a score of nothing at cricket, so called from the shape of the figure 0.

6. Water is called brackish, and the word means rather salt.

7. Not altogether. Even during the Ice Age the country south of a line joining the Severn and Thames estuaries was free from permanent ice.

8. Delilah cut off the hair of Samson (Judges xvi).

9. Alchemy was a primitive form of chemistry. The alchemists were chiefly concerned with finding the philosopher's stone that would change base metals into gold, and the elixir of life that would keep people young for ever, but in doing this they made discoveries in chemistry proper.

10. A grace-note in music is one introduced as an embellishment, which is not essential to the harmony or melody.

47

1. The distance is twenty-two miles, the time an hour and a half.

2. When a man was knighted in the Middle Ages, the person who dubbed him presented him with a pair of gilt spurs, which only knights could wear. The phrase 'to win one's spurs' was specially used of gaining knighthood by an act of valour on the field of battle, and now it means to achieve one's first honours. At the battle of Crécy Edward, the Black

Prince, was being defeated, but his father, Edward III, refused to send help saying, so the story goes, 'Let the boy win his spurs'.

3. Swallows in early autumn assemble on telegraph wires and the like before they migrate, that is, fly away to a warmer country. The best-known migrants besides the swallow family are the cuckoo and the nightingale, though there are many others. There are also many birds that migrate to us during the autumn from countries farther north.

4. The cherubim and seraphim are two orders of angels. We read about them in the Bible.

5. Antony (or Julius Caesar) and Cleopatra; Romeo and Juliet; Paris and Helen of Troy.

6. In Rome.

7. This is the biological name for the human species.

8. Aston Villa, with seven victories.

9. Avocado (pear), dado, bastinado, tornado, bravado; lumbago, archipelago, virago, farrago, sago.

10. You are dismissed (or at any rate you leave your work) and receive the insurance cards that have to be stamped every week.

48

1. The city of Winnipeg in Canada.

2. The lupin was originally blue, but plant breeders have produced lupins of many different colours – red, yellow, pink, white, purple, and some, particularly the Russell lupins, containing two different colours.

3. They are both arranged alphabetically, but a dictionary contains short articles giving information about different aspects of every word in the language (within reason) and in particular its meaning, and an encyclopaedia contains longer articles giving information on all branches of knowledge.

4. Ankara is the capital of Turkey; an earlier form is Angora, after which the Angora goat, rabbit and cat are named.

5. A radiographer takes X-ray photographs, and a radiotherapist treats diseases by X-rays.

6. Someone connected with the film industry. An Oscar is a gold-plated statuette awarded to film actors, directors, etc., for the best performance of the year in their particular line.

7. It is a cricket expression meaning that a batsman is not out at the end of his side's innings when all ten wickets have fallen.

8. Their tails were cut off by the farmer's wife.

9. There is no such year; the year 1 B.C. was followed by A.D. 1.

10. A shepherd is a sheep-herd, a man who looks after sheep. Herd is found by itself as a name, and there are Hoggart (or hog-herd), Seward (or sow-herd), Lambert (or lamb-herd), and Calvert (or calf-herd). Coward is usually another spelling of cow-herd, and does not indicate that the man to whom the name was first given was a coward.

49

1. It can be powered by a man, an animal (pony or donkey), or by an electrically or fuel driven engine.

2. An animal. Its plural is mongooses.

3. England, Scotland and Wales.

4. Rip Van Winkle slept for twenty years and when he awoke he found everything greatly changed. He lived in the Kaatskill Mountains in what is now the State of New York, and one of the changes during his sleep was that the United States had become independent of the British Empire.

5. Yes, the game played in a bowling alley. But it was the game of nine-pins (sometimes called skittles); the modern game is ten-pin bowling.

6. An inquest is an inquiry, especially the inquiry held by a coroner to find out the cause of a death which, it is thought, may have been due to violence or accident, or about which there is something suspicious.

7. It would mean that, although the drug penicillin (which kills bacteria) usually has no harmful effect on a patient, this particular person reacts to it abnormally, so that it might be dangerous to give it to him.

8. There have been eight Henrys, four Williams, and six Georges; so the total is eighteen.

9. Diocese and cathedral.

10. In thunder-storm clouds (cumulo nimbus) there are violent ascending and descending air currents, which are sometimes strong enough to damage aircraft. Frequently, falling rain is caught in one of these upgoing currents and rapidly ascends many thousands of feet. Hail stones may be formed in this process, when the rain reaches a height where the drops are frozen and fall as hail stones.

1. It is an area in which, by order of the local council, no fuel (like ordinary coal) can be burnt which causes smoke.

2. A shrub is smaller than a tree, and has several woody stems growing from the one root; a tree has one main stem or trunk, from which branches usually develop some distance above the ground. But the term is sometimes used loosely and applied to large shrubs.

3. Bowls is played on a green; large wooden balls are rolled towards a small white jack, and the players whose bowls finish nearest to this win the game.

4. Samarkand is a town in Western Asia in Turkestan, now part of the U.S.S.R. The road was called golden because it crossed the yellow sands of the desert, but chiefly because it was used by merchants who made gold from their trading.

5. It is a waltz written in Vienna by Johann Strauss the younger.

6. No; it would feel scalding hot.

7. Sherry takes its name from Xeres, now Jerez, in Spain, and port from Oporto in Portugal.

8. Bonn; Berlin.

9. (a) Barometer; (b) thermometer; (c) micrometer.

10. Siamese twins are born with their bodies partially joined together. They take their name from the first well-known pair who were born in Siam in 1829.

1. The term is used of a small speedboat moving very quickly and skimming along the surface of the water, or a person on a flat piece of wood being towed behind a fast-moving boat.

2. A parody is an imitation for the purpose of making fun of a piece of writing or pointing out its faults. The Mad Hatter gave this parody:

> 'Twinkle, twinkle, little bat!
> How I wonder what you're at!
> Up above the world you fly,
> Like a tea-tray in the sky.'

3. An off-licence is a shop licensed for the sale of intoxicants to be consumed off the premises; that is, they must not be drunk in the shop.

4. Parrots, mynahs, and budgerigars are the common ones.

5. A pibroch is properly the name of a tune, often war-like, played on the bag-pipe, though it is also used of the bag-pipe itself.

6. They are examples of rhyming slang. 'Rosie Lee' is tea and 'plates of meat' feet, but in the others the rhyming word has been dropped; in full it would be 'tit-for-tat' rhyming with 'hat'; 'apples and pears' rhyming with 'stairs'; and 'butcher's hook' rhyming with 'look'. 'Plates' alone is often used for feet.

7. To the west.

8. J. L. MacAdam (1756–1836) was an engineer who built many turnpike roads by the new method of making into a solid mass layers of stones of almost uniform size. From his name come 'macadamize', 'tarmacadam', and the trade name 'tarmac'.

9. Henry VII.

10. A tonsure is the shaven circular patch on top of the head of a monk or priest.

52

1. Antonio and Othello (in the plays by Shakespeare).

2. It has patches of black and white feathers clearly to be seen when it is flying. It also has a very long tail.

3. The West End, that part of London lying west of Charing Cross, was the fashionable quarter and now is the centre of entertainment; the East End is the part where the poorer classes live, sometimes still in slums. The phrases are often used of other towns.

4. The violin.

5. You should wear something white or at any rate light-coloured; if your clothes are dark, a strip of white cloth or a fluorescent arm-band round the arm will help. You may shine a torch, and it is advisable to walk on the right, so that you can see on-coming traffic.

6. California.

7. They were the Black Death, which reached England in 1349, and the Plague of London in 1665. The disease was spread by fleas which lived on rats.

8. A batsman scores six runs if the ball pitches over and clear of the boundary line or fence. He can also score six if there is an overthrow or a lost ball, and it is theoretically possible to run six before the ball crosses the boundary.

9. She wants you to give her a silver coin and then she will tell your fortune.

10. Retort.

53

1. He would be on board a yacht; a spinnaker is a large three-cornered sail.

2. D. D. Eisenhower, J. F. Kennedy, L. B. Johnson, R. M. Nixon.

3. It is not for a cat, but it is for a dog unless it is a sheep-dog or a guide-dog for a blind person, or is being used for sporting purposes or is one of a pack of hounds.

4. The Isles are the Hebrides which lie off the west coast of Scotland.

5. A Strad is a violin made by the famous maker Stradivarius (1644–1737) of Cremona in Italy.

6. They are soft-soled shoes which we sometimes call plimsolls or gym shoes.

7. The boat-race between Oxford and Cambridge Universities.

8. It is a railway with the carriages running on, and sometimes suspended from, a single rail.

9. A type of bacteria.

10. (a) Constable; (b) concave; (c) cone (or possibly conker); (d) Congress; (e) conquer; (f) confectionery; (g) concert; (h) conceal; (i) conger; (j) concertina.

1. A gymkhana is a fête comprising various events chiefly connected with horses and ponies. It has no connexion with gymnasium; the first comes from Hindustani, the second from Greek.

2. It is an animal, like a kangaroo, which has a pouch in which to carry its young.

3. Yes.

4. Both were possible during the Old Stone Age.

5. There are many you may think of; some of them are deer, emit, edit, star, stab, leek, meed, tram, garb, nuts, leer, teem, tang, part.

6. The difference is a matter of density. Haze is a thin mist which makes distant objects indistinct and is often due to heat; mist is a light fog. A photographic plate or film is said to be fogged when unwanted light has reached it and blackened the emulsion.

7. White clothes are cooler than black ones. Black surfaces absorb heat whereas white surfaces reflect a good deal of it.

8. It is a tree – the araucaria – so called because its many tough spikes would puzzle even a monkey that wanted to climb it.

9. In percussion instruments the sound is produced by hitting a stretched membrane or a hard surface of metal or wood. Examples of the first are the drum and tambourine, and of the second the cymbals, triangle, gong, bells, glockenspiel and xylophone.

10. Polyphemus was the chief of the Cyclops, one-eyed giants living in what is supposed to be the island of Sicily. He was visited by Ulysses and his companions and put them into a

cave, the entrance of which he blocked with a huge stone.
Ulysses made Polyphemus drunk, and put out his eye with a
firebrand, and he and his men escaped by hiding under the
bellies of the rams that Polyphemus let out to feed.

55

1. A wind from the west has come across the Atlantic ocean
and is generally more likely to bring rain than one from the
east. So the Lancashire side of the Pennines is wetter than
the Yorkshire side.

2. They are short for '*répondez s'il vous plaît* – 'please send an
answer'.

3. A siphon is a pipe or tube used for drawing liquid over the
edge of a vessel and delivering it at a lower level. It is bent
so that one leg is longer than the other; the tube is filled with
the liquid, the longer leg is closed with the finger and the
shorter leg plunged in the liquid. When the finger is removed
the liquid flows through the tube because of the difference
of the pressure of the liquid at the two ends of the tube.
There is also the soda-water siphon, which works by the
pressure of the gas which it contains.

4. It is a little under one inch.

5. He would mean that he had a puncture in his car tyre.

6. When a bird is ringed a small metal band is placed round
its leg; on this are recorded the date and the place. Then if
the bird is caught again we can ascertain how far it has
flown and similar information.

7. 'Drake he's in his hammock an' a thousand mile away'.
He's 'dreaming arl the time o' Plymouth Hoe'. ('Drake's
Drum' by Sir Henry Newbolt.)

189

8. The olive is grown in the countries round the Mediterranean Sea. The most important thing obtained from its fruit is the oil used in cooking.

9. (a) Bucharest; (b) buccaneer; (c) buck; (d) Buckinghamshire; (e) buckle.

10. 'And for auld lang syne, my dear,
For auld lang syne,
We'll tak a cup o' kindness yet,
For auld lang syne.'

56

1. *The Colditz Story* by P. R. Reid tells of an escape from the prison-camp at Colditz during the Second World War. Another book about a similar escape is *The Wooden Horse* by Eric Williams.

2. In China.

3. Simon Templar.

4. Members of the tit family – the most common being the blue and the great tit.

5. It should be the Isle of Wight.

6. The fuselage is the body of an aeroplane.

7. Mrs Beeton is famous for a cookery book which, published long ago in 1861, has been many times revised and is still much used.

8. Stencilling is a method of making letters or patterns by brushing colour through holes cut out of a piece of metal or card.

9. Harold Wilson in both years.

10. Margarine is made from oil – whale oil, or vegetable oil from groundnuts, cotton-seed, coconuts, soya beans, palm kernels, and sunflower seeds.

1. A mammoth is an extinct species of large elephant with a shaggy coat; its remains are often found preserved by the cold in Siberia. The word is used nowadays to mean 'very large'.

2. To Balmoral in Scotland.

3. William Tell is supposed to have lived in Switzerland in the fourteenth century, and to have resisted the Austrian rulers. For this he was arrested and required to hit with an arrow an apple which was put on the head of his little son. This he did successfully.

4. The thickness of knitting-wool.

5. Guy-ropes are used to keep something steady or to hold it in position. They are used in particular to keep tents erect.

6. (a) Charles Marshall, William Bright. (b) Cousins. (c) Sisters-in-law. (d) Grandson. (e) Nephew.

7. Criminal Investigation Department; Federal Bureau of Investigation.

8. A long-distance telephone call.

9. They are mountains in the Andes in Ecuador.

10. On the rugby field. The England team are called the Lions, the South African team the Springboks, and the Australia team the Wallabies.

58

1. An anorak is a hooded waterproof outer jacket: the word comes from the language spoken in Greenland, where it means a fur coat.

2. By desert.

3. January – snow; February – rain, lake; March – breezes, daffodil; April – primrose, daisies; May – dams; June – roses. (These are the words in the poem; sometimes others are satisfactory, like 'pond' for 'lake'.)

4. Field Marshal, Admiral of the Fleet, Marshal of the R.A.F.

5. No, it should be *A Midsummer Night's Dream*.

6. Augustus Caesar; Queen Victoria.

7. On Exmoor and Dartmoor, and in the New Forest.

8. The Jews. To them, all people who are not Jews are Gentiles.

9. (a) Midas. (b) Francis Drake on his circumnavigation of the world. (c) Fiftieth anniversary. (d) Its too greedy owner who could not wait for it to lay its eggs. (e) All that glisters (or glitters) is not gold.

10. The Cresta Run is at St Moritz; it is used for toboggans.

1. In Britain the first floor of a house is the one above the ground floor; in the U.S.A. it is generally the ground floor.

2. Dahlia and nasturtium.

3. Perseus killed Medusa, a Gorgon who turned to stone everything she looked at; he also slew a monster in order to rescue Andromeda.

4. Red Square, where is the tomb of Lenin.

5. (a) How many degrees are there in the angles of a triangle? (b) What is the formula for finding the circumference of a circle? (c) What is the formula for the area of a triangle?

6. The tattoo is the beating of a drum in the evening to call soldiers to their quarters, and also a military fête at night, often by torch light. To tattoo a person is to prick a design on the skin of his body.

7. She was a creature of extremes.

> 'When she was good, she was very, very good,
> But when she was bad, she was horrid.'

8. A desert rat is a red jerboa, a small animal of the rodent family; it was the badge of the 7th Armoured Division which fought in the desert in North Africa in the Second World War, and the phrase was applied to a man of this division.

9. A motor-car.

10. In this country Conservative, Labour and Liberal; in the U.S.A. Democrat and Republican.

1. Left, right; right, wrong.

2. A bench-mark shows a bar above a broad arrow and indicates that the height above sea-level at that point has been measured and is recorded on Ordnance Survey maps. The mark is usually cut into a wall a few inches above ground level.

3. 'Inferno' is the Italian word for hell and is the title of one of the parts of Dante's poem *The Divine Comedy*, in which the poet describes his visit to the underworld.

4. Kiev and Riga.

5. Glastonbury Abbey was supposed to have been founded by Joseph of Arimathea, the man who gave the tomb in which the body of Jesus Christ was placed. His staff was planted in the ground and became the Glastonbury Thorn which flowered at Christmas. Glastonbury was sometimes identified with Avalon, 'The Isle of the Blessed', and it was said that the tomb of King Arthur and Queen Guinevere was discovered there in the reign of Henry II.

6. No, though if we go back far enough, men and monkeys have a common ancestor.

7. An Italian air-line.

8. Hans Andersen wrote the story, in which the ugly duckling turns out to be a swan.

9. It is one-quarter.

10. You would be having a holiday on a canal or a river.

1. The names mean the seventh, eighth, ninth and tenth months, but the months are actually the ninth, tenth, eleventh and twelfth. At one time the year began in March, and then these names were correct.

2. Haemorrhage is bleeding, especially dangerous internal bleeding.

3. Charcoal.

4. Turkey.

5. The common earwig has wings, but it seldom uses them for flying.

6. Versailles is near Paris; it was built for Louis XIV.

7. (a) Tennyson; (b) Keats; (c) Chaucer; (d) Milton; (e) Wordsworth.

8. The Cossacks live in Russia north of the Black Sea. They are famous for their horsemanship.

9. John the Baptist was the forerunner of Jesus Christ; he was executed by order of King Herod. John the Apostle was the disciple whom Jesus loved, and may be the author of the gospel called by his name and of the Book of the Revelation.

10. It is the foremost part of the army. The opposite is the rearguard.

1. Yes; otherwise there would be no acorns.

2. 'Genesis' means creation or origin, and the book contains an account of the creation of the world and of the origin of the Hebrew nation. 'Exodus' means departure, and it tells of the departure of the Israelites from Egypt.

3. Windsor Castle. Eton College is near it.

4. Dean Swift wrote *Gulliver's Travels*. In Lilliput there lived dwarfs and in Brobdingnag giants.

5. Flying saucers are disc-like objects which some people claim to have seen in the sky and even suppose to have come from outer space, perhaps from Mars. There seems to be no real proof that such things exist.

6. No, it is in the West Indies.

7. He would be a golfer or just possibly a man concerned with the upkeep of a golf course.

8. Stamps for the Channel Islands were issued during the German occupation in the Second World War, and in 1948 there was a special issue to commemorate the third anniversary of the liberation. There are regional issues for Guernsey, Jersey and the Isle of Man.

9. In mountainous districts where there are many visitors. It is used to carry people to the tops of mountains in cars attached to a moving cable.

10. (a) Newcastle. (b) Coventry. (c) Thames. (d) Cheshire.

1. Aberdeen is in Scotland and Aberystwyth in Wales. 'Aber' is the Celtic word for mouth, and Scottish and Welsh names beginning with it indicate a town that stands at the mouth of a river.

2. Navy blue, with red piping.

3. Edward V and his brother are said to have been smothered in the Tower by order of their uncle who became Richard III. Whether the story is true is doubtful. (There is a very interesting novel about it by Josephine Tey, called *The Daughter of Time*.)

4. You see riding-lights hung on the rigging at night when a ship is riding at anchor.

5. To provide the vitamin C that they need.

6. 'Quick' here means 'living'. The quick is the living part of the nail, and if we cut this we are 'hurt to the quick'. A quicksand is as it were a living sand; a quickset hedge is a hedge of living plants as opposed to a fence; quicksilver (or mercury) seems alive as it moves about.

7. A spiral staircase curves round and round as it goes up.

8. The umpire calls 'Play' before the first ball is bowled at cricket. Hockey begins with a bully-off.

9. Lord Snowdon (Antony Armstrong-Jones).

10. (a) When did King Wenceslas look out? (b) Whom did he see?

1. The Roman Wall, built by order of the Emperor Hadrian, runs from Newcastle to Carlisle. The Great Wall of China also was built to keep out barbarians.

2. The Beast compelled Beauty to marry him by threatening her father with death. By agreeing, Beauty released him from a spell and he turned into a handsome prince.

3. 'Walking the plank' was a way in which pirates in the seventeenth century got rid of their prisoners. A plank was run out from the ship, and the prisoner walked along it blindfold until he stepped off the end and was drowned.

4. Jersey.

5. Port Said is on the Suez Canal, and Colon on the Panama Canal.

6. A back-seat driver is someone who is not himself driving the car but insists on telling the driver what to do.

7. British Broadcasting Corporation.

8. On the east side of Trafalgar Square in London.

9. A blunderbuss is an obsolete hand-gun, having a short barrel with a large bore. It fired a number of slugs and did execution at short range, but could not be aimed accurately.

10. You would look on the sea-shore.

1. Zebra crossings are shown by flashing amber beacons on the pavement at either side, and by broad black and white stripes on the crossings themselves. A pedestrian has the right of way once he is actually on the crossing.

2. The husband of Eve was Adam; they lived in the Garden of Eden. Eve persuaded Adam to eat a fruit that had been forbidden them by God – usually said to have been an apple. They were turned out of the Garden as a punishment.

3. The Jolly Roger was the skull and cross-bones flag flown by pirates.

4. The female cuckoo.

5. Lancaster, Leamington, Leeds, Leicester, Lincoln, Liverpool, London, Loughborough, Luton.

6. Chop suey is a Chinese dish, made up of meat, rice, etc., fried in sesame oil.

7. (a) Bungalow. (b) Flat. (c) Castle. (d) Igloo. (e) Caravan.

8. Belle Vue is an entertainment centre in Manchester containing, among many other things, a zoo. At Whipsnade, north of London, is an extension of the London Zoo.

9. Rudyard Kipling wrote one of his *Just-So* stories about the Elephant's Child whose great fault was his ''satiable curtiosity'.

10. They had a compass, so they could tell with a fair degree of accuracy when the sun was due south. When the sun is in this position it is midday, but with British Summer Time this would be 1 p.m. Another fairly reliable method would be to take note of their shadows. At 1 p.m. (B.S.T.) the sun

is at its highest point in the sky, and the shadows are shortest. They would not know that the shadows had been at their shortest until they were beginning to grow again, so this would not be as reliable as the first method, but it would work without a compass.

66

1. Yes, when the driver in front has signalled that he is going to turn right and you can overtake on the left without inconveniencing other traffic; when you are filtering to the left at a junction; and in slow-moving traffic when vehicles in the lane on your right are moving more slowly than you are.

2. His Chief Defect was 'chewing little bits of string'. He swallowed a piece which 'tied itself in ugly knots inside' and killed him (according to the poem by Hilaire Belloc).

3. It is usually pronounced 'shumak'. The sumach is a tree which grew originally in North America, and it is largely responsible for the brilliant colours seen in the forests there in the autumn.

4. William I. Charles Kingsley wrote a novel called *Hereward the Wake*. 'Wake' here means watchful or alert.

5. One only.

6. Octave means a set of eight; if you strike an octave you strike a note and the seventh note above it, so that there are six white notes between your thumb and finger.

7. Eurovision is the European television network.

8. A sleeper is a sleeping-car, and also a piece of timber or metal used as a support for rails.

9. Geography is the study of the surface of the earth and its inhabitants, and geology the study of the rocks that form the earth's crust.

10. In India.

67

1. It is to avoid the need to make a right-hand turn and so hold up the heavy traffic coming from the other direction.

2. Chatsworth, a mansion owned by the Duke of Devonshire, is in Derbyshire in the Peak District.

3. Privet is grown chiefly to make a hedge. Other plants used for this purpose are box, hawthorn, beech, holly, lonicera nitida, and yew.

4. You should make sure that the current is switched off; otherwise, you yourself may receive a shock when you touch the injured person.

5. In Spain.

6. A white elephant is properly something whose maintenance is more than it is worth. It is said that the King of Siam would present a white elephant – a sacred animal – to a courtier whom he wished to ruin with the cost of its upkeep. Nowadays however the phrase generally means no more than an unwanted possession.

7. A man makes his will so that his property after his death will be disposed of according to his wishes.

8. Boxing: the rules of boxing were drawn up in 1867 under the supervision of the Marquess of Queensberry.

9. Mercury, Venus, the Earth, Mars, Jupiter, Saturn, Neptune, Uranus and Pluto are the planets of the solar system.

10. (a) Etruria, to the north of Rome. (b) Rome. (c) The stand made by Horatius and his two friends to prevent the Etruscans from crossing (before it was hewn down) the bridge that led to Rome.

68

1. The Magi saw a star which led them to Bethlehem, to the infant Jesus. They took with them gold, frankincense and myrrh.

2. Shivering is a reflex action. When we run or do any physical exercise we become warmer. This is because the muscles are working, and when the muscles are working they produce heat. When we are cold the brain tells the muscles to work in an effort to produce heat, and they cause shivering.

3. Foods are ravioli, little envelopes of pasta with a savoury filling; and scampi, large prawns. Non-foods are alibi, a plea in law that the accused was elsewhere when the crime was committed; lapis lazuli, a semi-precious stone; and spermaceti, a white waxy substance obtained from the sperm whale.

4. (a) W. E. Gladstone. (b) Sir Winston Churchill.

5. Red is on the hot water tap, and blue on the cold water tap.

6. Flint.

7. An amateur can receive no money for playing, apart from his expenses. The game is his livelihood to a professional.

8. Galileo Galilei (1564–1642) was an Italian scientist who made the first practicable telescope. His beliefs brought him into conflict with the Inquisition, and he was compelled to deny the theory that the earth moves round the sun.

9. There must be two lamps – front and rear. Besides the rear light there must be a red reflector.

10. A torpedo is a missile sent from a submarine or other warship. It carries an explosive charge which goes off when it hits its target. (It is also a fish that is able to emit electric discharges to numb or kill its prey.)

69

1. The temperature may reach 90° F on a really hot day, and once at Greenwich Observatory on 9 August 1911, it reached 100° F.

2. (a) Lancashire and Westmorland. (b) Yorkshire and Durham.

3. The Amazons were a race of women warriors who the Greeks thought lived in Scythia north of the Black Sea. The river Amazon got its name because early Spanish explorers believed there were female warriors on its banks. Today the word is applied to any strong war-like or athletic woman.

4. The Air Show, and the Motor Show.

5. Fifteen all.

6. Big Ben tells us the time. It is the bell in the Clock Tower of the Houses of Parliament.

7. The eaves are the projecting edges of the roof. Eaves-dropping is listening for secrets – originally standing outside a house under the eaves in order to hear what is being said inside.

8. A lullaby is a song crooned to send a baby to sleep. The lullaby quoted continues –

> 'When the wind blows the cradle will rock;
> When the bough breaks the cradle will fall,
> Down will come baby, cradle and all'.

9. Maroon is a brownish-crimson colour; a maroon is a fire-work often used to give the alarm; maroons were fugitive Negro slaves living in the wild parts of the West Indies; and to maroon a person was to put him on a deserted island and leave him there for a punishment – as was done by the buccaneers.

10. The common ladybird is an insect – a little round beetle, red in colour with black spots. There is the rhyme

> 'Ladybird, ladybird,
> Fly away home,
> Your house is on fire,
> And your children all gone.'

70

1. The crawl.

2. Polar Bears are found only in the Arctic regions, and penguins only in the Antarctic.

3. Sir Henry Morgan (*c.* 1635–88) was a Welsh buccaneer.

4. People go to Lourdes on pilgrimages. In 1858 Bernadette Soubirous (St Bernadette), a peasant girl, claimed that the

Virgin Mary had appeared to her on eighteen occasions, and a spring that started at the same time began to attract invalids from all parts of the world hoping to be healed.

5. No. The Volga flows into the Caspian Sea, and the Danube into the Black Sea.

6. Agreements have been made with almost every state for a person accused of a crime to be extradited, or returned to this country for trial.

7. It must be held not later than five years after the previous election, but the Prime Minister may at any time advise the sovereign to dissolve Parliament so that an election can be held.

8. Mozart was a composer.

9. (a) Through thick and thin. (b) To go at something hammer and tongs. (c) To play fast and loose. (d) To fight tooth and nail. (e) Fits and starts.

10. The more formal kind of evening dress is 'a white tie and tails' – a long dress-coat with tails, a dress shirt and a white bow-tie; the other is a dinner jacket without tails, a dress shirt and a black bow-tie.

71

1. An insulator is a non-conductor of electricity, made of glass or porcelain, used to support electricity wires but not carrying off the current.

2. A yashmak is a thick veil over the face leaving only the eyes uncovered. It is worn, though not so commonly now as in earlier times, by women in Mohammedan countries like Turkey and Arabia.

3. Chlorophyll is the green colouring matter found in vegetation.

4. Buenos Aires – Argentina; Chicago – U.S.A.; Lyons – France; Milan – Italy; Yokohama – Japan.

5. Fanatic.

6. Shorthand (Pitman's.) It says 'This sentence is written in Pitman's shorthand.'

7. Mac and O' both mean 'son of' – as in Macdonald, son of Donald, and O'Neil, son of Neil. Names of similar meaning are formed from the English 'son' as in Robinson, son of Robin; and the Norman-French 'fitz' as in Fitzgerald, son of Gerald. The Welsh name Pritchard is derived from Ap Richard; Ap again means 'son of', and other Welsh names beginning with P have a similar meaning.

8. Old Stone Age, New Stone Age, Bronze Age, Iron Age.

9. July – showers, flowers; August – sheaves, corn; September fruit, sportsmen; October – pheasant, nuts; November – blast, leaves; December – sleet, blazing.

10. They are short for the Latin words *libra* (a pound), *solidus* (a shilling), and *denarius* (a penny).

72

1. It is the English Channel, though it would be more accurate to say the Straits of Dover. The first man to swim the Channel was Captain Matthew Webb in August 1875.

2. 'Tele-' means at a distance, and all the words you think of should have that as part of their meaning – telegram, telepathy, telephone, telescope, television, telephoto (lens).

3. Cyclone, hurricane, tornado, typhoon, whirlwind.

4. A brace and bit is used to bore a hole in wood.

5. At Kew are the famous Botanical Gardens, in which are grown plants from all over the world. The poet says 'go down to Kew in lilac-time'.

6. A flame needs oxygen in order to burn. As it burns it uses the oxygen in the air. Because the heater was in an airtight space, it went out when all the oxygen had been used.

7. 'All creatures great and small,
   All things wise and wonderful,
   The Lord God made them all'.

8. A name of this sort arose because the name of the lord of the manor in feudal times was added to the original name of the place, perhaps for the sake of distinguishing it from other villages of the same name.

9. Coral is a hard substance formed by the accumulation of the skeletons of minute sea-creatures. It is found forming reefs in warm seas, especially in the Pacific Ocean.

10. Full evening dress. (See the answer to question 10 of set 70.)

73

1. Mortar is used to join bricks together in a wall, and putty to fasten a pane of window-glass in its frame.

2. The one who went to Dundee. Dundalk is in Ireland, and Dunkirk in France, so that the other two would be drowned if they tried to walk.

3. 'Burying the hatchet' means making peace. It was a ceremony

of the North American Indians to show that a war was over. They had another ceremony from which we take the phrase 'smoking the pipe of peace'.

4. The legend was that a Jewish cobbler named Ahasuerus refused to allow Jesus to rest at his door while He was carrying the cross to the place of crucifixion. The Ancient Mariner killed an albatross, an action which the sailors believed would bring punishment.

5. Epsom – horse racing; Lords – cricket; St Andrew's – golf; Twickenham – Rugby football; Wimbledon – tennis.

6. Pompeii, not far from Vesuvius, was completely buried beneath lava from this volcano (A.D. 79).

7. The House of Commons, and the House of Lords. They are situated at Westminster.

8. Gossamer is made up of very fine spider-threads that form webs on bushes, in particular on calm mornings in autumn.

9. King David.

10. A dance very popular in the nineteen-twenties, and still common today.

74

1. Cotton-wool is a form of cotton; bees-wax is made by bees.

2. We see the lightning before we hear the thunder, because light travels faster than sound.

3. The Babylonians made marks on clay tablets which were then baked; the Egyptians wrote on papyrus made from the pith of reeds.

4. (a) Collapse; (b) colleague; (c) college; (d) colon; (e) colonel; (f) collide.

5. The man who brings the action is the plaintiff, and the defendant is the man against whom the action is brought.

6. Yes.

7. (a) Mackerel because it is not a fresh-water fish.
   (b) Fir because it is not a deciduous tree.
   (c) Tyrone because it is not a county in Scotland.

8. Mr Grimes, Tom's master, made him climb up chimneys in order to sweep them.

9. Holland.

10. Roland and Oliver were two of the paladins, or knights, of the Emperor Charlemagne. They fought one another for five successive days without either gaining the least advantage. To give a Roland for an Oliver now means to give tit for tat, to give as good as you receive.

75

1. (a) Architect; (b) sculptor; (c) dramatist or playwright.

2. A group of islands to the south-west of India.

3. Pewter is a metal, an alloy of tin and lead; beer-tankards were made from it.

4. The Reformation, which led to the setting-up of the Protestant churches.

5. A protractor is in the form of a half-circle and is used for measuring angles and laying them down on paper.

6. It was soccer. In rugger one point alone cannot be scored; it is unlikely that a score at cricket would be so low; and at tennis there are always more than three matches played. It might be hockey, but this is not often played by boys.

7. Everyone has two parents, four grandparents, eight great-grandparents, and sixteen great-great-grandparents – unless there are cousins amongst them, in which case the number would be reduced.

8. If you dislocate a joint you put it out of joint; if a hand is amputated it is cut off by a surgeon.

9. At the head of a monarchy is a king or a queen, who has inherited the title and keeps it until death; at the head of a republic is a president who is elected for a limited period.

10.   (a) Flopsy, Peter. (The little rabbits in *Peter Rabbit* by Beatrix Potter.)
    (b) Hearts, diamonds. (The suits at cards.)
    (c) George IV, William IV. (British Sovereigns of the nineteenth century).

76

1. *Viva voce* (Latin) means literally 'by the living voice', that is, 'orally'; a *viva voce* examination is an oral examination. *Sotto voce* (Italian) means 'below the voice' – 'in an undertone' or 'aside'. *Vice versa* (Latin) means 'the other way round'.

2. The group is the Heptarchy – the seven Anglo-Saxon Kingdoms of East Anglia, Essex, Kent, Mercia, Northumbria, Sussex and Wessex.

3. (a) A police car or an ambulance going to an emergency.
(b) A fire-engine.

4. If you looked directly at the window you would see the advertisement backwards; it would be reflected the right way round, and so it would read forwards in the mirror.

5. There are twelve members of a jury; twelve hours in a day and twelve months in the year; the twelve signs of the zodiac; twelve inches in a foot and twelve pence in a shilling; the twelve apostles; the twelve labours of Hercules; the twelve days of Christmas.

6. Camouflage means the disguising of objects used in war – guns, a camp, etc. – by paint, smoke-screens, netting etc. It was first used on a large scale during the First World War. It was to avoid detection by the enemy, especially by enemy aircraft.

7. The Pobble had no toes, but the Dong had a luminous nose.

8. Soft wood comes from evergreen trees, and hard wood from deciduous trees.

9. 'Starting from scratch' is starting in a race without being given any advantage, and 'scratching' is withdrawing from the race. These phrases are often used metaphorically.

10. The American continents are named after Amerigo Vespucci, who claimed that he was the first man to reach the American mainland in 1497. The people were called Indians because the first explorers believed that they had reached the neighbourhood of India.

77

1. When an animal or bird moults it sheds some of its fur or feathers.

2. The phrase 'hat trick' was first applied to the taking of

three wickets at cricket in consecutive balls. It is said that at one time a bowler who did this was given a new hat at the expense of the club. Nowadays the phrase is used more generally of, for instance, a footballer who scores three goals in one game.

3. *The Canterbury Tales* is a series of poems by Geoffrey Chaucer, the first great English poet. They were supposed to be told by pilgrims going to Canterbury to worship at the shrine of St Thomas à Becket.

4. It is in Italy. (Actually it is the airport for Rome.) The name is appropriate because Leonardo is one of the greatest of all Italians, and because, besides being a great painter, he was deeply interested in science and, as far back as the fifteenth century, developed the theory of flying in heavier-than-air machines.

5. Yes: trolley buses, small delivery vans, and vehicles (like milk floats) controlled by a man as he walks.

6. No, they reckon in dollars and cents.

7. Gethsemane was a garden just outside Jerusalem. It was here that Jesus Christ was betrayed by Judas Iscariot to his enemies.

8. (a) Newcastle-upon-Tyne. (b) Berwick-upon-Tweed. (c) Kingston-upon-Hull, usually called Hull. (d) In the full form they all contain the name of the river on which the town is situated.

9. A crescendo is a gradual increase in loudness; so the music could not rise to it. The word is pronounced 'kreshendo'.

10. The American sheriff is the official of a county charged with the duty of maintaining peace and order, guarding prisoners, etc. In the Middle Ages the sheriff was the king's

representative in a shire and governed it for him, in particular looking after his property in it.

78

1. Pythagoras is famous as a mathematician (and also as a philosopher).

2. Archbishop or bishop.

3. To blaze a trail is to mark it by chipping pieces of bark off the trees. But a blaze was originally a white mark on the forehead of a horse (the mark on the tree resembles this) and it still has this meaning.

4. Brightlingsea, Hornsea, Southsea, Swansea, Winchelsea, Withernsea. Chelsea and Battersea, although not strictly towns, could perhaps be included.

5. The port-hole.

6. Sir W. S. Gilbert collaborated with Sir A. S. Sullivan, the composer, to write the Savoy Operas - *H.M.S. Pinafore*, *The Pirates of Penzance*, *Patience*, *Iolanthe*, *Princess Ida*, *The Mikado*, *Ruddigore*, *The Yeomen of the Guard* and *The Gondoliers*.

7. Spain, and the Mediterranean Sea.

8. You can tell by the spelling; in England it would by 'fibre-glass' and 'mould'.

9. Making a more or less circular journey which ends at the same place as it began. In America, however, it means a return trip – a journey to a place and back again.

10. The little quantity of air inside the balloon expands and the balloon swells up.

1. Seals are mammals. They are to be found round the northern shores of Great Britain, and occasionally in the Thames estuary and off the eastern coasts.

2. The Ashes are played for at cricket between England and Australia.

3. A palette is a thin board, often of mahogany, with a thumbhole; on it a painter in oils mixes his colours. A water-colour painter's palette is made of porcelain, plastic or metal.

4. It means to pay for one's voyage on a ship by doing work on it.

5. (a) Gables. (b) Heron. (c) Limberlost. (d) Robe.

6. No, though there is nothing in the constitution to prevent it.

7. The Alps.

8. John Gilpin. The poem tells of his misadventures as he rode to Edmonton to celebrate his wedding anniversary.

9. Yes.

10. In 1215 King John put his seal to Magna Carta on the island of Runnymede in the River Thames.

1. A man goes bankrupt when he cannot pay his debts. He negotiates with the people to whom he owes money, and offers to pay a part of the debt; they, knowing that they cannot get the full amount, accept what is offered, and the bankrupt man is not liable to pay any more.

2. The Elephant and Castle is an area in south London; Broadway is in New York, and Pennsylvania Avenue is in Washington.

3. A safety belt prevents you from being thrown forward violently against the front of the car if it is stopped suddenly in a crash.

4. Cacti grow in hot dry countries.

5. At present it is fifteen (to be exact, at the end of the spring or summer term after the child becomes fifteen); in 1973 it will be raised to sixteen.

6. In Rome in ancient times.

7. Hogmanay is the Scottish name for the last day of the year, an occasion for celebrating. Haggis is a Scottish dish eaten especially at hogmanay. It is made of the heart, lungs and liver of a sheep, chopped up with suet, onions and oatmeal, seasoned and boiled in a sheep's stomach-bag.

8. He ordered Sir Patrick Spens to sail

> 'To Noroway o'er the faem,
> The king's daughter to Noroway,
> 'Tis thou maun bring her hame.'

9. Kicking the ball over the touch-line (the side-line) at rugby or association football.

10. There are four boys and three girls.

81

1. Chalk.

2. A unicorn had the legs of a buck, the tail of a lion, the head and body of a horse, and a single horn in the middle of its

forehead. Such a creature does not exist, but it is thought that the idea of its having a single horn comes from the great Indian rhinoceros.

3. 55 B.C. – landing of Julius Caesar; 1415 – Battle of Agincourt; 1485 – Battle of Bosworth; Henry VII became king; 1945 – end of Second World War.

4. The draught of a boat is the depth of water which a boat needs to float it. It must be known to the person navigating; otherwise he might run the boat aground in water too shallow for it.

5. Brer Rabbit in the stories told by Uncle Remus (in the book by Joel Chandler Harris).

6. Christians – cathedral, church or chapel; Jews – synagogue; Mohammedans – mosque.

7. He will miss the train by 5 minutes. If the train is the 10 a.m., he will try to arrive when his watch reads 10 a.m., because he believes it is only 10 to 10. Actually it is 5 past 10 and the train has departed.

8. Only Devon.

9. Yes, all those who are south of the equator.

10. The stars and other heavenly bodies.

82

1. Most types of willow grow in moist places, such as the banks of rivers. Cricket-bats are made from one species.

2. (a) They are novels by Charles Dickens.
   (b) They are the authors of children's books.
   (c) They are animals which are the central figures in books read by children – Babar, an elephant; Orlando, a cat; White Fang, a dog.

3. Etna, Hecla and Vesuvius are active; Fujiyama and Popocatepetl are dormant.

4. In the Middle Ages the women of the family had to spin flax or wool into yarn, and it used to be said that no young woman was fit to be a wife until she had spun for herself a set of body, table and bed linen, So a girl before marriage was called a spinster – a female spinner.

5. The event is the Olympic Games; the city omitted is Rome where the Games were held in 1960.

6. Only the eldest son of the reigning sovereign is made Prince of Wales. This is Prince Charles at present.

7. Roman Catholicism.

8. Jaguar, leopard, lion, lynx, ocelot, puma, tiger. Also of course the wild cat itself, sometimes found in the far north of Scotland.

9. The bow is the front, and the stern the back.

10. 139. (1 + 6 + 10 + 50 + 72.)

83

1. Horatio Hornblower when he is boarding his first ship, the *Justinian* (*Mr Midshipman Hornblower* by C. S. Forester).

2. On a chess board at the beginning of a game.

3. In 1789 began the French Revolution, and in 1917 the Russian Revolution.

4. Connie – Constance; Jim – James; Molly – Mary; Peggy – Margaret; Penny – Penelope; Ted – Edward.

5. It is flowing east.

6. It has been driven in a foreign country, where the plate **GB** indicates that it comes from Great Britain; the owner has not taken it off since his return to this country.

7. Early to bed and early to rise
   Makes a man healthy, and wealthy and wise.

8. Priest, parson, clergyman, vicar, rector, curate, padre.

9. We eat the leaves of brussels sprouts, cabbage, lettuce, mustard and cress, spinach and water-cress; and also of herbs like mint, parsley, sage and thyme.

10. Locusts.

84

1. There is no such creature as a mermaid, supposed to be half woman and half fish. The first part of the word means sea.

2. *Blitz* is the German word for lightning. The Germans in the Second World War had the word *blitzkrieg* – lightning war – to indicate their method of sudden attack. We came to use the first part of the word to mean an attack from the air, and then any sudden fierce attack.

3. Alice at the Mad Hatter's Tea-Party, when she was in Wonderland.

4. Spanish and Portuguese.

5. The ruff was worn round the neck; the wimple is folded so as to cover the head, the chin and the sides of the face and neck.

6. 'Old Glory' is the flag of the United States, also called the Stars and Stripes and the Star-Spangled Banner.

7. (a) Phosphorus; (b) camphor, soap, or any detergent.

8. One of them might be bad, and we do not want all the others to be tainted.

9. Yes, the goal-keeper.

10. Blackpool – Tower; Durham – Cathedral; London – The Strand; Rugby – School; Plymouth – The Hoe.

85

1. A jay is a bird with brilliant colouring; the word came to be used of a foolish person, and a jay-walker is a careless pedestrian who does not look out for traffic.

2. Asia is a continent, not a country; it has no capital.

3. (a) Plumber; (b) librarian; (c) stevedore or docker; (d) conductor.

4. Groynes are walls of timber running down the beach into the sea. They are built to prevent the movement of the sea along the coast from carrying pebbles and sand along with

it. Their effect is seen in the difference of the height of the material on either side of them.

5. Falcons were hawks trained to pursue and kill other birds. They were carried on the wrist and released when the prey was in sight.

6. The Orient is the east, the place where the sun rises, and to us in Western Europe it means China and Japan in particular. The opposite is the Occident, the part where the sun sets.

7. A spray of millet.

8. Old Mother Hubbard had a hungry dog, Little Boy Blue was warned the cow was in the corn, a fine lady upon a white horse was seen at Banbury Cross, Mary had a little lamb, and little boys are made of frogs and snails and puppy dogs' tails.

9. Yes, about 106 boys to 100 girls.

10. If we see an optical illusion, we do not see things as they really are; our eyes have deceived us.

86

1. Homer is the name of the great Greek poet to whom are ascribed the Iliad and the Odyssey. It also means a homing pigeon. (In the United States it means a home run at baseball.)

2. On the south coast.

3. By Van Gogh.

4. Queen Elizabeth succeeded to the throne on 6 February

1952; so if you were born after that date you were born in her reign, and if before it, in the reign of George VI.

5. We get steaks from cows and bullocks (beef steaks); and chops from sheep and pigs (lamb or mutton and pork chops.)

6. You might telephone, but only if the other person (or possibly a neighbour) had the telephone in his house. You might send a telegram, but this can only be delivered during certain hours of the day. You might send the message by car if a car and driver were available.

7. It means winning the best of three (or five) games; that is, to win two games out of three, or three games out of five.

8. Marquetry is a method of making designs or pictures by inlaying woods of various colours. A marquis is a nobleman next to a duke in rank. A marquee is a large tent.

9. The age of a tree can be found, when it has been cut down, by counting the number of rings in a cross-section; each ring is the result of one year's growth. In a living tree, it can be found by taking a boring across the girth of the tree.

10. Beer, champagne, cider, rum, sherry, vodka and whisky are all intoxicating drinks.

87

1. 'Heaping coals of fire on somebody's head' means returning good for evil in the hope of making the other person sorry for what he has done. 'Taking the lion's share' is taking the whole or greater part of something. 'Holding out the olive branch' is making an offer of peace.

2. Finisterre means the end of the land. The other Cape of course is Land's End.

3. The height of horses.

4. Sir Prudent received twelve payments: £1, £2, £4, £8, £16, £32, £64, £128, £256, £512, £1,024, and £2,048. This totals £4,095, so he chose wisely!

5. Three score years and ten, that is seventy years.

6. On Boxing Day only in Scotland, on Good Friday in all parts.

7. Leaf tobacco.

8. Malaria is spread by mosquitoes, which breed in stagnant water.

9. (a) No. They are very good for the soil. By their burrowing they help to drain it; they break it up and bring fresh soil to the surface; they bury leaves to rot away and enrich the soil. (b) No; if there is no disease on it, it may be composted and rotted down so that it can be spread on the garden and return nourishment to it.

10. The cottage is at Shottery near Stratford-on-Avon. It is visited because Anne became the wife of Shakespeare.

88

1. Noah built an Ark to save himself, his family and two of every kind of animal from the flood that had been prophesied.

2. (a) Pansy; (b) delphinium; (c) nasturtium; (d) hollyhock; (e) marigold.

3. The launching ground for space satellites and rockets. (It used to be called Cape Canaveral.)

4. Badger, deer, fox.

5.

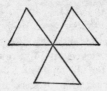

6. The pentathlon is an athletic contest of five events. For men these are the long jump, the javelin, the 200 metres, the discus and the 1500 metres all in one day; for women at the 1964 Olympic Games they were the 80 metres hurdles, the shot and the high jump on the first day, and the long jump and the 200 metres on the second. There is also the decathlon, a series of ten events – the 100 metres, the long jump, the shot, the high jump and the 400 metres on the first day, and the 110 metres hurdles, the discus, the pole vault, the javelin and the 1500 metres on the second.

7. Sulphuretted hydrogen. (Hydrogen Sulphide).

8. Rice.

9. On the east coast – Scarborough and Great Yarmouth; on the west coast – Blackpool; on the south coast – Bournemouth, Brighton and Torquay.

10. The trout; Malvolio.

89

1. A grass widow is a wife whose husband is away for some time, and a grass widower is a husband in similar circumstances. A wallflower is a woman at a dance who has no partner and sits by the wall.

2. In New Zealand.

3. The Norman Conquest.

4. A photo-finish is the finish of a race which is so close that the winner can be picked out only from a photograph taken automatically as the finishing line is crossed.

5. A tyre valve and the parts near by become warm when the tyre is being inflated. When the tyre is deflated by letting the air out a cooling takes place. When air is compressed it becomes warmer, and when compressed air is released it becomes cooler.

6. Novels – *Oliver Twist, Silas Marner*; plays – *Peter Pan, Waiting for Godot, Under Milk Wood*; poem – *Kubla Khan*.

7. Yes, the record is 1,606 m.p.h. by Lt.-Col. Robert R. Robinson, 22 November 1961.

8. A man insures his house so that if it is damaged or destroyed the insurance company will make up the loss. He pays the company a small sum of money every year, and the company bears the risk for him.

9. Bradford and Leeds; Chesterfield and Sheffield; Ipswich and Norwich; Liverpool and Manchester; Portsmouth and Southampton.

10. 'Old Master' is a rather vague term applied to the great painters of the period from the thirteenth to the sixteenth centuries, especially the Italians and the Dutch.

90

1. The district was the Weald between the North and South Downs. This was partly because iron-ore was mined not

far away, but chiefly because coal in the Middle Ages could not be used for smelting iron, and ample supplies of wood for making charcoal were needed. These were available from the forests of the Weald.

2. The United States, Australia, Canada and New Zealand.

3. (a) No. (b) No. (c) Probably.

4. Step-sisters; pumpkin; prince; twelve; slippers; glass.

5. The newly-built capital of Brazil.

6. King's College Chapel, Cambridge.

7. The Colossus was a great statue on the island of Rhodes in the eastern Mediterranean. According to legend, its feet rested on either side of the harbour entrance so that ships had to sail between its legs. From this come our words 'colossal' – enormous, and Coliseum.

8. (a) (Sir) Winston Churchill. (b) Harold Wilson.

9. John Peel, who lived at Troutbeck in the Lake District.

10. Steel.

91

1. Helen Keller lost both sight and hearing from scarlet fever when she was nineteen months old. She learnt the finger alphabet, how to read and write and later how to speak. She became a graduate of Radcliffe College in 1904. She died in 1968, aged 87.

2. The Archbishop of Canterbury crowns the king (or queen) in Westminster Abbey.

3. Beard, feared, weird; bird, furred, heard, whirred, word.

4. The vintage is properly the gathering of grapes for wine-making, and a vintage wine has come to mean the wine of a good year. So a vintage car is an old car of a make with a reputation for high quality, comparable with a vintage wine. A car is considered to be a vintage model if it was manufactured between 1919 and 1930.

5. The Australian aborigines used boomerangs, which if they hit nothing circled round and returned to the thrower.

6. A Hercules is a very strong man; Hercules was a Greek hero possessed of superhuman vigour and strength. A Solomon is a very wise man; King Solomon asked God for wisdom and became famous for it.

7. Billy Bunter.

8. Horse-chestnut, horse-radish, horse-tail.

9. They are both bones in the lower part of the leg below the knee.

10. Costa Brava – Spain; Riviera – France or Italy; fjords – Norway; Trossachs – Scotland.

92

1. Daffodil of Wales, rose of England, shamrock of Ireland, thistle of Scotland.

2. On the prairies of North America.

3. They are the capitals of Dominions of the British Commonwealth – Australia, Canada and New Zealand.

4. Acceleration is an increase in speed. Thus, the speed of a car might be 40 m.p.h., and it would accelerate to 50 m.p.h.

5. Yes, the Hop, Step and Jump, now called the Triple Jump.

6. Only iron.

7. Scrooge, who saw the ghost of his dead partner Marley, and the spirits of Christmas Past, Christmas Present, and Christmas Yet To Come.

8. Sir Henry Wood after 1895. They are generally called the Proms.

9. Milton became blind and Beethoven deaf.

10. The phrase is 'to discuss the pros and cons'. It means to discuss the arguments for and against. Pro means 'in favour of', and con is short for 'contra', against.

93

1. *Bon jour*.

2. The Kaiser ruled in Germany before the First World War. 'Kaiser' is a form of 'Caesar', whose name in Roman times became used as the title of the Emperor of the West.

3. No, the Austin Mini is just over ten feet.

4. Hengist and Horsa are supposed to have led the Anglo-Saxons who landed in Kent and began the conquest of Britain.

5. We eat the fruit of the tomato plant and the stem of rhubarb.

6. The trident is a three-pronged spear (and also the name of an aeroplane). Neptune and Britannia are represented as holding one.

7. Dunkery Beacon is on Exmoor and Kinder Scout in the Peak District of Derbyshire.

8. The 'gate' is the number of people paying to see a football or cricket match, and the 'house' is the audience at a theatre or cinema.

9. They all are except the vizier, and by our constitution the prime minister.

10. Yes, it is 20 fluid ounces against the 16 ounces of the American pint.

94

1. The robin. The bird's chest becomes a brighter red in autumn.

2. Bread, cereals, chipped potatoes, chocolate, sugar.

3. Bricks are made of clay. To make bricks without straw is to try to do something without having the necessary materials. In ancient Egypt straw was used to bind the mud used for making bricks. The Israelites, when they were bondsmen in Egypt, had to make so many bricks each day, and then were ordered to make the same number and also to find the straw (Exodus, v, 7).

4. (a) Great Britain is larger in population, Canada in size.
   (b) Italy is larger in both.
   (c) The U.S.S.R. is larger in both.

5. The Pilgrim Fathers sailed to America in 1620 and landed at Plymouth in Massachusetts.

6. Football. It is a famous club in Spain.

7. (a) Contour lines. (b) Isotherms.

8. The Danes settled chiefly in the east, in particular in Lincolnshire and Yorkshire. The endings are -by as in Whitby, and -thorpe as in Mablethorpe. By means village, and thorpe hamlet.

9. Yes. Fold the paper in pleats (each pleat about ½ inch) and then place the narrow ends of the paper (with the zigzag) on the two bricks. The paper will then support the jar of water, since corrugated material is stronger than flat.

10. A valve on a bicycle tyre allows the air to flow in one direction only. It is opened by the pressure of the air, the air passes through, and the valve then closes to prevent the air from going back. There are valves in our heart and at the beginning of our arteries to prevent the blood which is being pumped round from flowing backwards.

95

1. Sir Christopher Wren designed St Paul's, which Ludgate Hill leads up to.

2. A hydrofoil is a device on a speedboat for raising it from the water as its speed increases. A hovercraft is a vehicle that moves along a very small distance above the surface of the ground or water, being supported on a cushion of air from jet engines.

3. Before the Anglo-Saxon conquest the proper name is Britain; only after it should the country be called England — the land of the Angles.

4. Sponges are animal. The ones we wash with are the skeletons of sea-creatures.

5. Europe, Asia, North America, South America, Africa, Australasia and Antarctica.

6. Because of better weapons. Iron is a harder metal than bronze, but bronze, an alloy of copper and tin, is better than stone.

7. An ostrich is said to bury its head in the sand, thinking that, because it cannot see danger, there is none.

8. Aqualung (as it were a lung for using under water); aqua-planing (see set 51, no. 1.); aquamarine (the bluish-green colour of sea water); aquarium (a tank of water for keeping fish, etc., in); aquatic (living in water). There is also aque-duct (a channel or pipe for conveying water across a valley.)

9. The first team of a school or club is playing an eleven chosen from all the other members.

10. The Brook, in a poem by Lord Tennyson. The Brook joins 'the brimming river'.

96

1. They are in New York.

2. Lava is the rock from a volcanic eruption, whether it is molten and flowing down the mountain-side, or solidified. A larva is an insect in the grub stage.

3. A gallon of petrol costs something over 6s. The quantity a tank can hold varies in different cars from twenty gallons to little more than five.

4. The carnation and the lily of the valley are scented; so are most of the old roses, but many of the new varieties are not.

5. By sleeping on twenty feather-beds and twenty mattresses; underneath them all was a pea, and her skin was so sensitive that she could feel the pea, and her whole body became black and blue with bruises.

6. They are all names of British wild flowers.

7. The offing is a nautical term for the region some distance off shore; when something is in the offing it is in sight. Making a landfall is coming within sight of land after a voyage in the open sea.

8. No.

9. Yes.

10. You would get coffee and rolls (or *croissants*). The meal is called *le goûter* or *le five-o'clock*.

97

1. (a) Four is not a prime number. (b) Golf is not a team game. (It is also played all the year round.) (c) Keats was a poet, not a novelist.

2. Bombay and Cairo are north of the equator; the rest are south.

3. Spion Kop is a hill in South Africa where a battle was fought (1900) in the Second Boer War. The mounds are named after this.

4. Holyhead, on Holy Island, off Anglesey.

5. Under an ash, maple or sycamore tree. Keys are the fruit of these trees and fly through the air when they are ripe and fall.

6. As a painter.

7. Horse-drawn carts, bicycles, tricycles and prams.

8. Watling Street began at Dover and ran through London to Chester.

9. An X-ray photograph is taken.

10. Barts is St Bartholomew's Hospital in London founded in 1123. Bart is short for baronet, the lowest title that is handed down from father to son.

98

1. In Loch Ness in Inverness-shire.

2. Sea.

3. Peat is found in moors and bogs especially in Ireland; it is made up of soil and half-decayed vegetable matter. It is dried and used as fuel; it is also incorporated in the soil in the garden to lighten and enrich it, and to enable it to retain moisture.

4. (a) Yes. (b) Yes.

5. Before Christ; *Anno Domini* (in the year of our Lord); *ante meridiem* (before noon); *post meridiem* (after noon).

6. The sparrow with his bow and arrow killed Cock Robin; the fly with his little eye saw him die.

7. A little south-east.

8. To play possum is to lie low. Possum is short for opossum, an American animal that tries to avoid capture by pretending to be dead.

9. James VI of Scotland became James I of England. His mother was Mary Queen of Scots.

10. Only the *Daily Telegraph*. It is *The Times* not *The Daily Times*, and the *Daily News* no longer exists.

99

1. XCIX.

2. Alexandria – Egypt; Calcutta – India; Durban – South Africa; Rio de Janeiro – Brazil; Haifa – Israel.

3. June – 'flaming' June.

4. No, for it is mostly covered in ice and snow. It is said that the Norwegian Eric the Red, who explored the country, gave it its name in order to make people more willing to go there to settle.

5. (a) Greengrocer or fruiterer. (b) Newsagent. (c) Grocer. (d) Baker or confectioner. (e) Butcher.

6. Cook Strait is between North and South Islands of New Zealand. It is named after Captain Cook, the South Sea explorer.

7. A garage is a building where motor-vehicles are housed, but it also now means an establishment where petrol is sold and cars can be cleaned, repaired, and otherwise attended to. A hangar is a shed where aeroplanes are housed.

8. Bush in Australia; pampas in South America south of the Amazon; savannahs in tropical America; tundra in the Arctic regions; veld in South Africa.

9. The Derby is the most famous of English horse-races, run on Epsom Downs about Whitsuntide. A local Derby is a match between two neighbouring teams.

10. Stockton and Darlington; Liverpool and Manchester; Rocket, George Stephenson.

100

1. (a) 112 (in U.S.A. 100). (b) Between England and France, from 1337 to 1453. (c) Very tiny sweets. (d) A hymn tune. ('All people that on earth do dwell' is sung to it.) (e) Billiards.

2. Plywood is made of three, five or seven layers of wood glued or cemented together under pressure, and arranged so that the grain of one layer runs at right angles to the grain of the next.

3. Trooping the Colour takes place at the Horse Guards Parade on the sovereign's official birthday, June 10th. Changing the Guard takes place before Buckingham Palace or St James's Palace every morning. (Mounting the Guard, also every morning, is at the Horse Guards Parade.)

4. Usually they did not sit on chairs, but on stools or benches.

5. A Bingo evening.

6. No, only Minnesota. There is no state called Columbia, though British Columbia is a province of Canada, and Colombia is a country in South America. Saskatchewan is another province of Canada.

7. The Isle of Man is not part of any English county; the Isle of Wight is part of Hampshire.

8. (a) 1588. (b) Philip II. (c) Spain. (d) Sir Francis Drake.

9. A doctor's patients, a lawyer's clients, a hotel-keeper's guests, a stationmaster's passengers.

10. The Last Post is sounded at night; it is the second of two bugle-calls denoting the hour of retiring. It is also sounded over a dead soldier at military funerals.

THE PUFFIN BOOK OF MAGIC

Norman Hunter

The magic in this book will not enable you to turn your school-teacher into a chocolate-cream frog, or cause a mighty palace to arise in the back garden. But it does show you how to perform exciting, amusing, mysterious and somewhat joyous conjuring tricks, to entertain your friends and cause them to think you no end of a clever chap (or girl, of course). It also shows you how to have a bit of fun making some of the things used in the tricks, without also making too much mess.

Norman Hunter, who conjured up the Professor Branestawm stories, has included several tricks that he performs in his own Chinese magic act, which he lets off under the name of Ho Wat Fun.

SOMETHING TO DO

Septima

Here at last is a book to fill up all the wet days and dull days that produce the question 'What can I do?' in every family. *Something To Do* has suggestions for things children can do at home, indoors and outside, without spending much money or being a terrible nuisance.

Each month has a separate chapter so that the games and ideas will fit in with the proper season. February, for instance, has a special section of Things To Do in Bed, and August, the holiday month, has a bunch of ideas to pass the time while travelling. Every month has its own special flower and bird to look for. There are tempting dishes to cook, things to make, games to play, and instructions for keeping pets.

THE EXPLOITS OF MOOMINPAPPA

Tove Jansson

One cold and windy autumn evening many years ago a newspaper parcel was found on the doorstep of the Home for Moomin Foundlings. Inside the parcel lay poor shivering little Moominpappa (as he was later to become).

The spring came, and Moominpappa decided to run away from the home and see what great events were awaiting him. Life is short, the world is enormous, and he simply couldn't stay in the home any longer. So off he went. And the friends who awaited him were people like Hodgkins of the hairy ears, the shy, jumpy Muddler, and Edward the colossal Booble, who was always trampling people underfoot and then conscientiously paying for their funerals. They were all rather eventful people, but the biggest event of all was when Moominpappa rescued a beautiful little Moomin woman from the waves, and discovered – Moominmamma.

THE CUSTER WOLF

Roger Caras

One April five wolf cubs were born in a cave under a tree stump. One was white, and men would come to call him by a name that would live in history, for this was the beginning of the legend of the Custer Wolf.

This wolf inexplicably grew up different from any other. He was a beautiful but solitary animal and as he grew it became clear that he killed for the love of killing and terrorised a huge area round the town of Custer for six whole years.

Sometimes he killed thirty cattle in a week, more than he could possibly eat, and he took incredible chances, yet he escaped every trap that was set and every gun that was fired. Small wonder that the men believed the white wolf was charmed.

If you have enjoyed this book and would like to know about others which we publish, why not join the Puffin Club?

You will be sent the Club magazine Puffin Post *four times a year and a smart badge and membership book. You will also be able to enter all the competitions. There is an application form overleaf.*

APPLICATION FOR MEMBERSHIP OF
THE PUFFIN CLUB

TO: THE PUFFIN CLUB SECRETARY,
PENGUIN BOOKS LTD,
HARMONDSWORTH, MIDDLESEX

Please enrol me in the Puffin Club. I enclose my subscription for:

(please tick appropriate box)

3 Year Membership (£1)* ☐

1 Year Membership (10s)* ☐

Family Membership (10s a year plus 2s 6d for each member)* ☐

Overseas Membership
School Membership } Please apply for further details

(*Write clearly in block letters*)

Christian Name(s)   Surname

Full Address (*Use a separate box for each line*)

Boy or Girl. . . . .   Date of Birth. . . . .

Signature . . . .

*Subject to alteration without prior notice